Hellebores

H. lividus

H. niger, the Christmas Rose

Hellebores

BRIAN MATHEW

Royal Botanic Gardens, Kew

ALPINE GARDEN SOCIETY

First published 1989

© Brian Mathew

Alpine Garden Society
Lye End Link, St John's
Woking
Surrey GU21 1SW

Editor: Richard Bird
Assistant Editor: Robert Rolfe
Designer: John Fitzmaurice

ISBN 0 900048 50 6

Typeset by Tradespools Ltd., Frome

Colour by Waterden Reproductions Ltd., London

Printed by W S Cowell Ltd, Ipswich

ACKNOWLEDGEMENTS

It is difficult to name in person all those who have contributed to my knowledge of Hellebores since there are so many friends and colleagues who have done so. However, in particular I offer my grateful thanks to Jim Archibald, Helen Ballard, Chris Brickell, Herbert and Molly Crook, Richard Nutt, Netta Statham, Elizabeth Strangman and Primrose Warburg for their generosity in sharing both their knowledge and plants with me. I must also acknowledge the great amount of help given to me in the past by those fine plantsmen E.B. Anderson, Eliot Hodgkin and Sir Frederick Stern.

This is also a suitable place to say how delighted I am to have the book so beautifully illustrated by Mary Grierson and to thank her for her extreme patience during the lengthy period of development of the text!

Contents

Foreword

When contemplating the prospects of writing a monograph of the genus Helleborus I was reminded of the following prayer:

> Lord thou knowest better than I know myself that I am growing older and will some day be old. Keep my mind free from the recital of endless details; give me wings to get to the point. I dare not ask for improved memory, but for a growing humility and a lessing cocksureness when my memory seems to clash with the memories of others. Teach me the glorious lesson that occasionally I may be mistaken. Amen.
>
> Extract from 17th century *Nun's prayer*

Having had an interest in Hellebores spanning some forty years I have at last come to the conclusion that this small, lovable, but infuriatingly difficult genus is almost impossible to classify! My love-hate relationship with Hellebores began when as a child I found a hybrid of the *H. orientalis* type on a rubbish tip near our home and brought it back into the garden. Soon there were rows of seedlings which I cherished, in happy ignorance of any need for names. This early love of Hellebores led later on in life to a series of memorable journeys in the Balkans and Turkey to study and collect them, but inevitably there came a time when identification was necessary and this is where the hate crept in, for it is now clear to me that there is no absolutely foolproof system of classification. So please, when reading through this work with a critical eye, spare a thought for the taxonomist who, at a fixed point in time on the constantly moving path of evolution, is expected to place all living things in perfect units with precise descriptions and indisputable names attached. Hellebores, to take but one example, do *not* conform!

It is, at first sight, surprising that this very popular group of plants should have been so neglected by the horticultural writers. In fact there is no recent book devoted to them and to glean much information at all one has to delve into diverse journals and elderly works, which are mainly in German and rather rare, so that access to a comprehensive botanical library is essential. I hasten to add that I am in no way criticising these works for they still form the basis for the classification of *Helleborus* and I am quite sure that no-one will improve on their approach in any fundamental way. Although there are no modern books on Hellebores to refer to, there are several botanical accounts, mainly in the various floras which cover the regions where they occur and these of course supply a great deal of valuable information, although they are often dramatically conflicting in the degree of 'splitting' or 'lumping'. The student of Hellebores may thus terminate his or her researches more confused than before!

My aim in writing this book has been to gather together a lot of the information which is so widely scattered, combine it with my own observations of Hellebores in the wild, in gardens and in various herbarium collections and provide the lovers of these fascinating garden-worthy plants with a handy reference book which is both informative and readable. We are fortunate in that one of the leading botanical artists of our time, Mary Grierson, has prepared the illustrations and I think you will agree that these beautiful plates enhance the book enormously, each capturing the essential details of the species, with various characteristic touches which make them more than just botanical portraits. With such highly variable plants it was not possible to illustrate a large range of forms of each species so it was decided to include colour photographs as well as paintings to improve the coverage and to give an indication of how they grow in the wild. It is often said that for artistic reasons paintings and photographs should not appear in the same book, but it is my opinion that in this case there is too much valuable information to be lost by excluding the photographs on the grounds of aesthetics.

I think it is probably true to say that nearly all growers of Hellebores are confused when it comes to the question of identification. It would be nice to think that I have clarified this position in some way but I fear that, as I have said above, there is no infallible way of classifying them. The only sure way would be to reduce the number of recognised species to about eight or nine so that, for example, all the green-flowered European Hellebores were housed under one name. This would, I think, be a most unfortunate step to take, of almost no practical value and almost certainly not representing the true state of affairs; few people, if any, would believe in such a system. On the other hand to split them into many species, subspecies, varieties and forms would be cumbersome in the extreme and would probably be ignored. In any case, this latter approach does not work, since even at the rank of *forma* there is still variation and overlap. The most tenable position is, I am sure, somewhere in the centre of these two extremes and it seems to me that there are in fact a number of distinct species which, at the periphery of each of their areas of distribution, merge in their characteristics with the next, probably through hybridisation. In one or two instances in Yugoslavia I have seen this happening quite clearly and my impression through studying herbarium material is that it happens in several other cases as well. Thus, we often find a sliding scale of variation from one species to the next with no hard and fast lines of demarcation. To impose a series of botanical names, which is for practical purposes essential if we are to communicate about plants, is difficult in such a genus.

My approach in this book has been to try to simplify matters by treating the most distinct 'units' as species and to indicate where there are overlaps. Within the species which I have recognised there is still considerable variation but this has been taken into account in the keys and in the descriptions. So please remember that many of the species Hellebores each have a lot of variants and there is not, for example, any one 'true' *H. orientalis*, *H. torquatus* or *H. multifidus*. It may be possible to find dozens of different variations, all belonging to the same species and all therefore equally entitled to the same name.

This ability of Hellebores to vary, although confusing and frustrating in some respects, does have its compensations, for it means that the horticulturist has much scope for selection and hybridisation, leading to aesthetically superior garden forms.

> Know ye the flower that just now blows,
> In the middle of winter – the Christmas rose –
>
> * * * * *
>
> Though it lack perfume to regale the nose
> To the eyes right fair is the Christmas rose –
> A Fiddlestick's end for the frost and snows;
> Sing hey, sing ho, for the Christmas rose.

> *Punch*, 30 December 1882

I

Hellebores and Herbalism

The name Hellebore has been associated with plants of medicinal interest for at least 2200 years and probably much longer, for Theophrastus (372–287 BC) used the name as if it were already well established in Greek history. To the ancient Greeks there were Black and White Hellebores, *Elleboros melas* and *Elleboros leucas*, but sadly we cannot be absolutely sure of the identity of these plants. The White Hellebore is generally reckoned to be what we now call *Veratrum album* and certainly this seems to be the best candidate, taking into account the available descriptions from old literature sources. *Veratrum* and *Helleborus* have been almost inextricably entwined in the herbals, linked by the vernacular name of Hellebore although they are of course completely different in appearance, the former a monocotyledon related to the Lilies and the latter a dicotyledon in the Ranunculaceae. Interestingly this nomenclatural link is not confined to one language, for Tournefort on his Turkish travels in about 1700 was informed that the medicinal root of *Helleborus orientalis* was called 'Zoplème', whereas today Çöpleme is the Turkish name for *Veratrum*. It does seem to me that there is enough evidence to exclude the White Hellebore of Theophrastus, and many other authors, from the genus *Helleborus* as we recognise it today and regard the name as most likely referring to *Veratrum*. Theophrastus encountered this confusion between the various plants called *Elleboros* and in his fascinating *Enquiry into Plants* remarked (I quote from Sir Arthur Hort's translation of 1916) that 'the White and Black Hellebore appear to have nothing in common except the name. But accounts differ as to the appearance of the plants; some say that the two are alike and differ only in colour, the root of the one being white, of the other black; some however say that the leaf of the black is like that of bay, that of the white like that of the leek, but that the roots are alike except for their respective colours'. He also noted that the stem to some extent resembled that of *Ferula* in being hollow, but this part of the description is presumably restricted to the White Hellebore, *Veratrum*. If Theophrastus, some 300 years BC, had already received jumbled information about their identity, there is little hope for us in trying to sort out the matter conclusively! Nevertheless it is of great interest to record the comments made by various classical authors concerning the appearance and value of Black Hellebore since there is considerable agreement with later herbalists over the uses of the plant.

Pliny the Elder (23–79 AD) in his 37 volume *History of the World*, or the *Natural History of Pliny*, gives a wealth of information about plants and their uses, although it is thought that the details are not always accurate. Nevertheless the material is highly valuable since it was culled from many other Greek and

Elleboros melas, the Black Hellebore, from Dioscorides, *Codex Vindobonensis Medicorum Graecorum* (c.77AD). The illustration, which clearly does not represent *Helleborus*, as we know it, was not in the original version and was added later by a Byzantine artist.

purgationis causa sumptitantur . Prodest morbis comitialibus, melancholicis , insanientibus, articularijs doloribus , & resolutis . Menses inditum trahit, partus necat : purgat fistulas impositum , & tertio die detractum . Item contra grauitatem auditus in aurem demittitur , ibíque in alterum , aut tertrium diem esse finitur . Scabiem sanat illitum cum thure, aut cera , & pice , & cedrino oleo : uitiliginibus, lepris , impetiginibus ex aceto medetur : dentium dolorem collutione mitigat . Erodentibus medicamentis commiscetur : hydropicorum uentri utilissimè imponitur factum ex eo, farina hordeacea, & uino, cataplasma . Consitum proximè radices uitium, uinum purgandi facultate donat . Huius resparsu domos expurgari arbitrantur : quare inter fodiendum stantes Apollinem, Aesculapiúmque precantur , ac uitant aquilae uolatus : aduolare enim non sine periculo tradant . nanque si ams effossionem ellebori conspexerit , moriturum qui succidit, augurium est . Celeriter effodiatur oportet , quoniam haliru caput aggrauat: quapropter ad id arcendum, fossuri allium praesumere, & uinum bibere consueuerunt : nulli ita noxae opportuni redduntur . Veratri albi modo emendatur .

ELLEBORVM NIGRVM ALTERVM.

H ?viridis, from Mattioli, *Commentarii in libros sex P. Dioscoridis Anazarbei de Medica Materia* (1554).

11

H. vesicarius in fruit; flower shown bottom left

H. vesicarius in cultivation

Photographs by B. Mathew except where stated.

H. vesicarius in fruit near Gaziantep, S. Turkey

Ἐλλέβορος μέλας. VERATRVM NIGRVM. CAP. CXLVI.

Elleborum nigrum appellatur melampodion, quoniam caprarum paftor nomine Melampus fu-
rentes in fe Prœtidas primus purgaffe, & fanaffe fertur. Folia ei uiridia, platani fimilia: minora,
folijs fphondylij proxima, fubafpera, nigriora, pluribus diuifuris incifa: caulis afper: flores in purpura
albicantes, racematim cohærentes: femen cnici, quod in Anticyra fefamoides uocant: quo deiecti-
ones moliuntur. Radicibus cohæret nigris, tenuibus, à capitulo confiftratis, quarum eft ufus.
In collibus, afperis, & a fitientibus locis enafcitur. Optimum eft, quod ex huiufmodi petitur terris, ut
ex Anticyra. Nigrum inibi probatiffimum gignitur. Eligi debet corpulentum, & plenum in quo re-
nuis fit medulla, acre, guftu, feruenfque: cuiufmodi eft in Helicone, Parnafo, & Ætolia natum: ata-
men Heliconium præcellit. Veratrum nigrum purgat uentrem, detrahit bilem pituitasque, datum
per fe, aut cum fcámonia, & tribus obolis fiue drachma falis. decoquitur uel cum lente, & iufculis, quæ

ELLEBORVM NIGRVM.

purgationis

H. *niger*, taken from Mattioli,
*Commentarii in libros sex P.
Dioscoridis Anazarbei de Medica
Materia* (1554), labelled *Elleboros
melas, Veratrum nigrum* and
Elleborum nigrum.

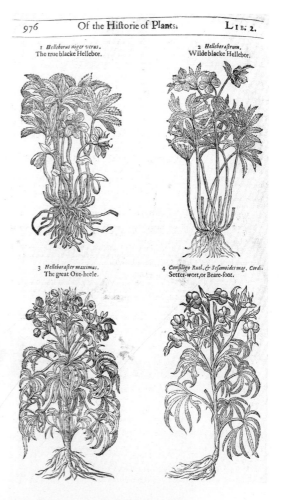

1 *Helleborus niger verus.*
The true blacke Hellebor.

2 *Helleboraftrum.*
Wilde blacke Hellebor.

3 *Helleboraſter maximus.*
The great Oxe-heele.

4 *Confiligo Ruel. & Sefamoides mag. Cord.*
Setter-wort, or Beare-foot.

Illustrations from John Gerard's
Herball, or Generall Historie of Plantes
(1636). H. *niger* (top left), H. *viridis*
(top right), H. *foetidus*, 2 forms
(bottom).

Roman works which are no longer in existence. Pliny's tomes were translated into English in the early 17th century by Philemon Holland, and I have purposely used passages from this edition since the language is so fascinating. On the question of identity Pliny says that 'two principall sorts there be of it; namely, the white and the blacke: which distinction of colour, most writers would have to be meant and understood of the roots onely, and no part els: others there be, who would have the root [presumably this is a mistake for leaf – BM] of the blacke Ellebore to be fashioned like unto those of the Plane tree, but that they be smaller and of a more darke and duskish greene, divided also into more jags and cuts'. Perhaps here we have some sort of indication of a divided leaf, and more like that of Hellebores as we know them, although the description is scarcely very convincing.

Pedanius Dioscorides (c. 40–90 AD) from Anazarbus in Cilicia is one of the better known of the Greek physician-pharmacologists and travelled as surgeon to Nero's armies, so would have been excellently placed for accumulating a wide knowledge of medical botany. His *De Materia Medica* (c. 77 AD) provided the main reference source on the subject for some 1500 or more years. Even so, it is clear that some of Dioscorides' work is based on that of Theophrastus who undoubtedly acquired information from even earlier sources. Plagiarism, one imagines, has flourished for as long as there has been the written word, and fortunately so in some cases, since the original sources are lost. Dioscorides' writings can still be consulted in their original Greek form since there is a beautiful Austrian facsimile edition of the *Codex Vindobonensis* (the Vienna manuscript), produced in the 1960s. However, for our purposes it is more convenient to refer to the English translation of John Goodyer (1655). This translation was never printed but happily was made available in 1934 when Robert T. Gunther produced a largely unchanged version, using Goodyer's 17th century English. The illustrations used in Dioscorides' Greek herbal were added by a Byzantine artist (perhaps more than one) at a slightly later date and although many of them are excellent and can be clearly recognised, other drawings appear to represent plants which have been 'designed by a committee'! The illustration of *Elleborus melas* (Black Hellebore) is most definitely not a Hellebore as we know it, having a bulb-like base with a tall stem bearing alternate deeply toothed leaves and small 5-petalled-flowers in the upper axils; a few long narrow basal leaves are shown as well, an unlikely combination of features. Exactly what this might be intended to represent I do not know. The accompanying description of the plant, which may be taken to be Dioscorides' original, reads (but in Goodyer's words), 'It hath leaves green like to ye Plane tree, but lesser, coming near to those of Spondylium, and more jagged, and blacker, and somewhat rough, ye stalk rough, but ye flowers white, inclining to purple, but in fashion like clusters, and in it a seed like to Cnicus, which also they who live in Anticyra call Sesamoeides, and use it for purgations: ye roots lie under, thin, black, hanging as it were upon an onion-like little head of which also there is use'. Here again, as with Pliny's description, there is little evidence to associate this description with the plant which we call *Helleborus* today. Nevertheless authors throughout the ages have equated the Black Hellebore of the ancients with *Helleborus* as we know it, and later versions of Dioscorides' 'De Materia Medica', for example that of Matthiolus (1565), carried perfectly recognisable illustrations of *Helleborus niger* and *H. viridis* or one of its relatives.

Later on we shall consider the medicinal and toxic properties of the ancient Greek *Elleboros melas* and review the various uses in the succeeding centuries, including the more recent analyses of the active chemicals involved. There is undoubtedly a marked degree of similarity in the herbals and medical dictionaries throughout the whole period as to the uses and effects of Black Hellebore and one feels that it must be the same plant which has been utilised for these sundry purposes for so long. Obviously some accounts agree because they are direct copies of statements made in earlier works, but not all. Although one can only speculate, it seems to me quite likely that the name *Elleboros* was a group name for a number of different species, probably belonging to different genera, which were brought together because of similar medicinal properties rather than a likeness in appearance. For practical purposes this approach would have been quite adequate for the users of such herbal remedies because they were only interested in the results. Similarly, the gatherers of the herbs would know which plants to collect which would produce the desired effects and may well have grouped together any which were similar in their properties, in this case combining the roots of several different species under the name of *Elleboros*. In fact we know that there were at least two, the black and the white, which were entirely different in appearance. The herbalists who recorded the data doubtless gleaned their information from a variety of sources so inevitably the descriptions given to them would, if this theory has any sound basis, be somewhat confused, referring to a range of species. Much later it was reported that the drug Black Hellebore was sometimes adulterated using *Aconitum*, *Adonis*, *Trollius* and *Actaea* roots. Is it possible that this supposed 'adulteration' was in fact based on an ancient tradition, and was quite intentional, and that these plants were mixed together because of their medicinal similarity?

The Hellebores of the later herbalists are not a source of confusion and quite clearly refer to the plants we know today under this name. John Gerard (1545-1612) is perhaps the most frequently quoted since his *Herball* is fairly readily accessible. Although a substantial part of his work is undoubtedly based on that of other writers, especially the Flemish botanist Dodoens (1583), and the illustrations were largely taken from Tabernaemontanus' *Eicones Plantarum seu stirpium* (1590), Gerard did add some important personal knowledge, and gives us a fascinating and lucid account of how the plants were used in the 16th century. In chapter 361 of *The Herball or Generall Historie of Plantes* (1567) there are three easily recognised drawings, (1) *Helleborus niger verus*, the True Blacke Hellebor, (2) *Helleborastrum*, the Wilde Blacke Hellebor and (3) *Helleboraster maximus*, The Great Oxeheele; these represent *H. niger*, *H. viridis* and *H. foetidus* in modern nomenclature. A fourth drawing labelled *Consiligo* or *Sesamoides magnum*, the Setterwoort or Bearfoote, is probably another form of *H. foetidus* although less easily recognisable. Gerard, rather significantly, notes that 'we have them all in our London gardens', indicating that his knowledge was by no means all based on the work of others. Interestingly, he distinguishes these four Hellebores from the plant which he considers to be the Hellebore of Dioscorides. In the next chapter, 362, entitled 'Of Dioscorides his blacke Hellebor' he gives a good description and illustration of the herbaceous umbellifer *Astrantia*, with the vernacular name of Black Masterwoorts. This is noted as having similar purgative effects to those of Hellebore, and later writers, for example Meyrick (1790), also describe the Black Masterwort and its usefulness as a violent purgative. Referring back to the descriptions by Pliny and Dioscorides, *Astrantia* has certain attractions as a possible candidate for the Black Hellebore of ancient Greece, although the illustration in Dioscorides' *Materia Medica*, which I mentioned before, bears no more resemblance to an *Astrantia* than it does to a *Helleborus*. Another point to note is that *Astrantia* species are not known in Greece although they do occur commonly in more northern parts of the Balkan peninsular, from Albania and Yugoslavia northwards, and may possibly just extend into the Pindus Mountains.

If the ancient Greeks were using a species of *Helleborus* medicinally then it is most likely to have been *H. cyclophyllus* which occurs commonly in central and northern parts of Greece. The flora of the country has probably not changed a great deal in just 2000 years so this is a reasonable assumption. *H. orientalis* would also have been known to them since it is widespread in western and northern Turkey, then part of the Greek empire.

Although we cannot be sure that the Black Hellebore drug of the ancients was derived from a species of *Helleborus* as we know it today, it is certain that the later European herbalist-botanists were fully aware of *Helleborus* and its usefulness and dangers, and it is significant that the properties they describe are not far removed from those claimed by the early Greek writers.

The name *Elleboros* is of unknown origin. The explanation most frequently offered is that it is derived from two Greek words meaning 'to kill' and 'food', referring to the poisonous substances they contain. This derivation has no great appeal since the ancients obviously regarded Hellebores as extremely useful plants and are hardly likely to have given them such a derogatory name. Another explanation is that the name is taken from an earlier Hebrew one, 'Helibar', but since Hellebores do not occur to the south or southeast of Turkey, any Hebrew or Egyptian source for the name seems a little unlikely. If the drug was traded in those early times the name for it would surely have been coined by those on whose territory it was to be found growing, rather than by the purchasers.

One wonders if the initial part of the name is connected with Ellas, the Greeks' name for their country, and boreas (borras) might refer to the north. Could it be that this name arose because *Helleborus* and *Veratrum* are more frequent in the north of the country especially in the Balkan countries to the north of Greece, and are absent altogether in the south? This is as unlikely a suggestion as the others but it perhaps adds something to the puzzle for someone more scholarly than I to ponder upon!

2

Toxicity of Hellebores and symptoms of poisoning

Modern analysis of the poisonous principles involved in Hellebore roots show that there are glycosides present which have been given names such as Helleborin, Helleborein, Hellebrin and Helleborigenin. Other substances have also been identified including Aconitic acid, Calcium phosphate, Starch, various fats and oils and several alkaloids which are known to have cardiac effects. Hellebrin causes the bitter taste which has been noted by several authors and is known to have a strong cardiac action, whereas Helleborin is reported to be less powerful in this respect but instead has a narcotic effect.

Writers throughout the ages have noted the poisonous nature of Black Hellebore. Some of the more recent works of this century are less melodramatic in their accounts than the earlier herbalists, noting that when touched, Hellebores may produce reddening of the skin or blisters, and if taken internally will result in vomiting, diarrhoea or paralysis. I can vouch for the fact that Hellebores are poisonous, at least to cows, as I relate later on page 55. There are plenty of other examples of death in animals caused by Hellebore poisoning and one cannot stress how important it is not to throw away Hellebore leaves in a place where they might be accessible to grazing animals. Human deaths have also been recorded from accidental overdoses but not in very recent times since the use of the drug has now ceased.

For those who feel the urge to try out any of the remedies mentioned in connection with Hellebores, the clear message is DON'T! In order to stress the importance of this, I quote a gruesome passage from Hamilton's *Flora Homoeopathica* (1852), since this will surely deter the most avid would-be herbalist!

> 'Two persons took a decoction of this root in cider; three quarters of an hour after taking it, alarming symptoms were developed, with exciting suspicion of the real cause. One of the men, therefore, took another dose, when vomiting, delirium, horrible convulsions, accompanied with immediate coldness, supervened, and death at last ensued. On dissection, sixteen hours afterwards, the appearance in each were found precisely similar, except that in the one who took the largest quantity they were more strongly marked; the lungs were gorged with blood; the mucous membrane of the stomach was considerably inflamed, of a blackish-brown colour, and reduced almost to a gangrenous state.'

Hamilton also notes that if administered to dogs it caused death in 16–18 hours, and in only 6 minutes in a rabbit. More recent accounts of death in animals show that Hamilton's observations were no exaggeration, and that similarly nasty effects could be caused when an external dressing of Hellebore was applied to kill lice, perhaps if the animal licked the dressing.

Pliny knew of the dangers and recorded that (in the words of Holland's 1601 translation) 'The black Ellebore is a very poison to horses, kine, oxen and swine, for it killeth them; and therefore naturally these beasts beware how they eat of it, whereas confidently they feed upon the white.' Theophrastus (Hort's translation 1916) also noted that 'the black is fatal to horses, oxen and pigs'.

In connection with human poisoning it is important to note the observations made by Tournefort on his travels in Turkey in the late 17th century since there is unquestionable evidence in the form of herbarium specimens that he was referring to *Helleborus orientalis* roots. His letters written on the journey were published in book form in 1718 as a *Voyage into the Levant* and make fascinating reading. I quote in full from the English version:

'We were acquainted with two Botanists at *Prussa* [= Bursa], one an *Emir*, the other an *Armenian*, who went for great Doctors. They furnish'd us with the Root of the true *Black Hellebore* of the Antients, in what quantity we would, to make an Extract. 'Tis the same Species with that of the *Anticyres*, and the Coasts of the *Black-Sea*. This Plant, which the *Turks* call *Zopléme*, and which is very common at the foot of Mount *Olympus* [= Ulu Dağ], has for its Root a Stump about the bigness of the Thumb, lying along, three or four inches in length, hard, woody, divided into several Roots, smaller and wreath'd. All these Parts put forth Shoots of two or three inches long, ending in reddish Eyes, or buds: But the Stump and the Subdivisions are blackish without, and whitish within. The Fibres which accompany them are bushy, eight or ten inches long, from one to two lines thick, little or nothing hairy. The oldest are black without, the others brown; the new ones white: One and t'other are of a brittle Flesh or Substance, without Sharpness or Smell; and a reddish Nerve runs through them. They smell like Bacon, when it's boiled in Water.

Out of twenty five Pounds of the Root, we drew two Pounds and a half of an Extract, brown, very bitter, and resinous. It purges taken alone, from twenty Grains to half a *Gros*. Three *Armenians*, to whom we gave it, all complained they were much troubled with *Nauseas*, Griping of the Guts, Heats, a Sharpness in the Stomach, along the *Oesophagus*, in the Throat and Fundament; of Cramps, Convulsive Motions, join'd with violent shooting Pains in the Head, which also return'd again some Days after. So that we abated one half of our Esteem for this great Remedy. As for the Roots, they must be us'd as those of our *Hellebore*, boiling them to the quantity of a *Gros*, or a *Gros* and a half, in Milk, letting them infuse the whole Night, warming the Milk in the morning the next Day, and straining it through a Cloth.

The *Turks* ascribe great Virtues to this Plant; but we could not learn them. *M. Anthony Cerci*, who has practised Physick a great while at *Constantinople*, *Cutaye*, and *Prussa*, told us he never us'd it, because of the Accidents which it brings upon sick People.'

As a final word on the toxic nature of Hellebores, one should mention that some people are affected when they touch the plants, for example when collecting seeds. A correspondent in the *Gardeners' Chronicle* in 1872 noted that he had raised hundreds of *H. foetidus* plants to provide cover for game in his woods. 'The men who planted the Hellebore complained to me the following day of their hands being sore, and of a disagreeable feeling of prickling and itchiness in their fingers and hands'. I have not experienced this myself, but Will Ingwersen once told me that he and his colleagues, whilst collecting seeds from *H. argutifolius* (*H. corsicus*) in Corsica, received some nasty effects, noting in the A.G.S. *Bulletin* 2: 182 (1934) that 'we became aware of an unpleasant feeling, akin to a violent nettle sting, in the tips of our fingers, and several hours afterwards our finger-tips were a mass of huge, very painful blisters'.

3

Medicinal uses of Hellebores through the ages

The active ingredients in Hellebores are, it appears, contained mainly in the roots, for it is usually the dried rhizomes and roots which are mentioned in the herbals, although Theophrastus indicates that the seeds were used as well. The more recent English medical books refer to the dried product as *Radix hellebori nigri* or *Hellebori nigri rhizoma* and this consisted mainly of *H. niger* roots imported from Germany. Sometimes an extract of the roots was prepared in proof spirit and used under the name of *Tinctura Hellebori*. The root is said to have a bitter acrid taste, causing a tingling sensation of the tongue. The range of problems treated with Hellebore was exceptionally wide and dealt with both internal and external troubles, so I have grouped these below depending upon their method of application.

Collecting Hellebore roots seems to have caused considerable problems for the early herbalists, Theophrastus noting that (in Hort's translation) it 'makes the hand heavy, and men cannot go on digging it up for long; wherefore they first eat garlic and take a draught of neat wine'. He continues, 'both root and fruit [seeds, presumably – BM] are useful for the same purposes, if it is true, as is said, that the people of Anticyra use the fruit as a purge; this fruit contains the well known drug called *sesamodes*.' Dioscorides (in Goodyer's translation) has stern warnings for those who do not observe the correct procedure. 'When they dig it, they stand praying to Apollo and Aesculapius, observing ye Eagles flight, for they say he flies that way not without danger to them. For ye bird causeth death, if so be he see ye digging of ye Hellebore.'

Certain areas were considered to yield a better quality Hellebore than others, and Theophrastus mentions that 'the black kind of Hellebore grows everywhere; it is found in Boeotia in Euboea and in many other places; but best is that from Mount Helicon'. Dioscorides gives us similar information, noting that 'It grows in rough and high, and dry places. And that is best which is taken out of such Countries, such as is that of Anticyra for the black and ye best grows in it. But chuse that which is fleshy, and well nourished having but a thin pith, sharp in ye taste, and burning. Such as is that in Helicon, and Parnassus, and that which grows in Aetolia. Yet that of Helicon is ye best' (taken from Goodyer's 1655 translation of *Materia Medica*). The ancient Greeks are said to have classified their drugs as first, second, third and fourth quality, often according to the source. There seems to have been a concensus of opinion that Anticyra was a good area, as were Mt. Helicon and Mt. Parnassus; on both of these mountains *H. cyclophyllus* is a relatively common plant. There were at least three places called Anticyra, one of which was near Mt. Parnassus and Mt. Helicon, so this seems a likely candidate. Anticyra was renowned in classical times as a place where the drug was prepared, and as a resort where people consulted physicians and were given a course of Hellebore treatment, usually for mental disorders. 'You should go to Anticyra' is reputed to have been a derogatory expression used to call into question a person's sanity!

Internal uses
As mentioned above, the Black Hellebore drug has been considered efficacious in the treatment of afflictions of the mind, and Pliny dwelt upon this at some length, commenting first upon the legend that King Proteus's daughters had been cured by it. The quotation is from Philemon Holland's 1601 translation of Pliny's *Natural History*.

> 'Who hath not heard of Melampus that famous divinour and prophet? He it was of whome one of the Ellebores took the name, and was called melampodion: and yet some there be who attribute the finding of that hearbe unto a shepheard or heardman of that name, who observing well that his shee goats feeding thereupon, fell a scouring, gave their milke unto the daughters of K. Proetus, whereby they were cured of their furious melancholie, and brought againe to their right wits.'

Pliny continues to extol the virtues of the Black Hellebore, noting that it 'is good for the palsie, for those that be lunaticke and bestraught in their wits, for such as be in a dropsie (so they be cleare of a fever,) for inveterat gouts as well of feet and hands as other joynts: it purgeth downward by the belly, both choller and fleame: being taken in water, it gently mollifieth and looseneth the bodie ... It is a most soveraigne remedie for the falling sickness, the swimming or dizzinesse of the head: it cureth malancholicke persons troubled in mind; such as be brainsicke, mad, lunaticke, phranticke, and furious: it is singular good for the Elephantie, the foule and dangerous morphew called Leuce, the filthie leprosie, and the generall convulsion whereby the bodie continueth stiffe and starke, as if it were all one peece without any joynt.' However, Pliny offers some words of caution, that 'this is a medicine that would not bee ministred inwardly to fearefull, timorous, and faint-hearted persons', nor to those of a 'foeminine and delicat bodie; as also to those that be in mind effeminat: likewise to those who are thin and slender, soft and tender.'

Dioscorides also recommends it for various mental disorders but has a few additional uses as well. Goodyer's translation (1655) of *De Materia Medica* (c. 77 AD) contains entertaining phraseology in an uninhibited style which is worthy of quotation: 'It purgeth ye belly from above, driving out Phlegm, and choler, being given by itself, or with Scammonie and Salt, ye quantity of a dragm, or three Oboli. It is sod [soaked] also with Lens, and broths which are taken for purging. It is good for ye Epilepticall, Melancholicall, frantick, Arthriticall, Paralyticall. But given in a Pessum, it expels ye menstrua and kills ye Embrya ... It is also put in corroding medecines. But with barley meal and wine, it is a Cataplasme good for ye Hydropicall. And being planted by vines near ye root, it makes ye wine made of them to be purgative.'

Most of these claims are repeated by later herbalists and we find that Gerard (1597) adds little to the ancient Greek recommendations, although he does

H. foetidus, a wild British form

H. foetidus 'Wester Flisk'

H. argutifolius in cultivation

H. argutifolius growing in Corsica.
(Photo: H & M Crook)

H. argutifolius habitat in Corsica.
(Photo: H & M Crook)

indicate that it was also used as a vermifuge. He says: 'A purgation of blacke Hellebor [in this case *H. niger*] is good for mad and furious men, for melancholike, dull, and heavie persons, for those that are troubled with the falling sicknesse, for lepers, for them that are sicke of a quartaine ague, and briefly for all those that are troubled with blacke choler, and molested with melancholie.

'The rootes take way the Morphew and blacke spots in the skin, tetters, ringwoormes, leprosies, and scabs. The roote sodden in pottage with flesh openeth the bellies of such as have the dropsie. The root of bastarde Hellebor (*H. viridis*), called among our English women Bearfoote, steeped in wine and drunken, looseth the belly, even as the true blacke Hellebor, and is good against all the diseases whereunto blacke Hellebor serveth, and killeth wormes in children. It doth this operation with more force and might, if it be made into powder, and a dram thereof be received in wine.'

The vermicidal properties of Hellebore were also written up by William Woodville in his *Medical Botany* (1790). He reports on the findings of a Dr Bisset of the Royal College of Physicians in London who noted that 'The great bastard black Hellebore or Bear's Foot, is by far the most powerful vermifuge for long round worms of any I have yet experienced. The anthelmintic virtue of this plant is well known to the vulgar in the Duchy of Cleveland, Yorkshire, who generally give it to their children when they suspect them to have worms'. It is also mentioned in this work that *H. foetidus* is useful in some cases of asthma.

W. Meyrick's *New Family Herbal** of 1790 contains interesting information, although much of it no doubt based on the experiences of earlier writers. Of the Black Hellebore, he writes 'Given in substance in doses of ten or fifteen grains, it purges roughly, and to such as are of robust habits, many prove serviceable in dropsical complaints ... Taken in smaller doses it promotes urine and perspiration, and is very much extolled for its singular efficacy in obstructions and suppression of the menses. It is likewise useful in all hesteric, nervous, and hypochondriacal complaints, and was at one time esteemed almost a specific for madness, but in that it appears to have greatly lost its credit'.

Hamilton in his *Flora Homoeopathica* (1852) gave dire warnings about the efficiency of Hellebore as a poison, as I have quoted above, but on the other hand added that it had been reported that it had cured hydrocephalus in a child, used in the form of a tincture, and that it was also a cardiac stimulant.

By the end of the 19th century some of the active elements in Hellebore roots had been identified, and their effects noted. In *Medicinal Plants* by R. Bentley and H. Trimen (1880), the glycosides which had been found were listed and there was an impressive array of complaints which were known to have been treated, including mania, melancholia, epilepsy, dropsy, amenorrhoea, dysmenorrhoea, skin infections and worms. By this time the Hellebore drug was largely derived from *H. niger*, although *H. viridis* and *H. foetidus* were also used to some extent. More recent works suggest that *H. viridis* may have a greater cardiac effect than *H. niger*, as a result of the presence of the glycoside Hellebrin. It is noted that

---

* The actual title of this is *The New Family Herbal or Domestic Physician: enumerating, with descriptions, all the known vegetables which are in any way remarkable for medical efficacy; with an account of their virtues in the several diseases incident to the human frame*!

Hellebrin regulates cardiac rhythm and is similar in its effect to the Digitalis group of drugs. Possibly these heart-stimulating properties account for the claim by Paracelsus (1490–1541) that the Black Hellebore 'is good for those of older years (i.e. over fifty). Gathered when the moon is in one of her signs of conservation, dried in an east wind, powdered and mixed with its own weight of sugar, it renders old people younger and more vigorous'. Paracelsus, however, was a controversial character whose views should probably be viewed with some suspicion, for he regularly upset his colleagues and frequently moved on from one European university to another, eventually, it is thought, coming to a rather sticky end at the hands of some of those he upset.

External uses

Although Hellebore was mainly used internally for a wide variety of ailments it was to some extent also recommended for external application for curing various blemishes. Pliny (Holland's translation, 1601) advised that it should be 'applied without the bodie in manner of a liniment with salted hogs grease' to cure 'flegmaticke wheals and pimples'. Dioscorides said (Goodyer's translation, 1655) that 'it cleanseth fistulaes being put into them, and taken away after ye third day. In like sort also it is put into ye ear for such as are hard of hearing, letting it alone for two or three days. It doth also heal ye Psoras, being anointed on with Franckincense, or wax and pitch and *Oleum Cedrinum*, and being laid on with Vinegar by itself, it heals ye Vitiligo, and ye Impetigo, and leprosies. But being sodden [soaked] with Acetum it assuageth toothaches, by washing ye mouth with it'.

In fact there would appear to be very few problems which Hellebore was not reputed to deal with!

As a pesticide

There are a few reports of Hellebore being used as a pesticide, for example as a powder to kill caterpillars on fruit bushes; one would, I imagine, have to be rather careful not to breathe in the dust. Pliny noted that if (I quote from Holland's translation) 'Ellebore be beaten to powder and strewde upon milke, all the lice that tast thereof will die. To conclude, the said milke is good to rid away lice, nits, and such like vermine out of the head and other parts of the bodie'. The use of Hellebore for this purpose seems to have been continued into the present century and it has been suggested that some of the deaths in animals may have been as a result of the creature licking off the ointment which had been applied to kill pests.

Veterinary uses

Apart from employing Hellebore as an insecticide as mentioned above, there were sundry other uses for the drug in veterinary medicine. The curious practice of inserting a piece of root into a hole made in the dewlap of cattle seems to have had a considerable following in Britain and Europe, and is described in Gerard's *Herball* (1597) in some detail. Speaking of *H. viridis* and *H. foetidus* he says 'Most name it *Consiligo*, bicause the husbandmen of our time do herewith cure their cattell, no otherwise than the olde Farriers or horseleeches were wont to do, that is, they cut a slit or hole in the dewlap, as they terme it (which is an emptie skin under the throte of the beast) wherein they put a peece of the roote of

Setterwort, or Bearfoote, suffering it there to remaine for certaine daies togither: which manner of curing they do call Settering of their cattell ... This manner of Settering of cattell, helpeth the disease of the lungs, the cough, and wheesing. Moreover, in the time of pestilence or murraine, or any other disease affecting cattell, they put the roote into the place aforesaid, which draweth unto it all the venemous matter, and voideth it foorth at the wound. The which Absyrtus and Hierocles the Greeke Horseleeches have at large set downe. And is called in English Bearfoote, Setterwoort and Settergrasse. The third and fourth [these are *H. foetidus* forms – BM] are named in the Germane toong Lowszkraut, that is Pedicularis, or Lowsie grasse: for it is thought to destroy and kill lyce'.

In view of all these amazing claims for the Black hellebore root it may be tempting to experiment but I must repeat that this is a very poisonous plant and on no account should any attempt be made to concoct home-made herbal remedies.

4

The Genus Helleborus Linnaeus,

Species Plantarum: 557 (1753)

Type species: *H. niger* L. (see page 66)

Helleborus, a small Old World genus of herbaceous perennials, is generally considered to belong to the family *Ranunculaceae*. The segregate family *Helleboraceae*, dating from Loiseleur (1819), has never gained widespread recognition although it was upheld by the great systematist Spach (1839), in whose system *Helleborus* was placed with *Eranthis* in the tribe *Helleboreae*, subtribe *Helleborineae*, and was also recognised as recently as 1973 by J. Hutchinson in his *Families of Flowering Plants*. It is the possession of several ovules in each of the carpels which separate *Helleborus*, and a number of other genera, from *Ranunculus* and its allies in which each carpel has only one ovule. However, the current opinion appears to be that these are insufficient grounds for creating separate families. The subdivisions within the *Ranunculaceae* vary somewhat from author to author, for example Bentham & Hooker (1862) regarded *Helleborus* as belonging to the tribe *Helleboreae*, subtribe *Caltheae* which included *Caltha*, *Trollius* and *Eranthis*. In the system of Airy Shaw (1973), based on an earlier one of Hutchinson, it is placed in the subfamily *Helleboroideae*, tribe *Helleboreae*, along with *Caltha*, *Trollius*, *Eranthis*, *Coptis*, *Isopyrum*, *Nigella*, *Actaea* and *Aquilegia*, all of which have regular flowers and fruits consisting of follicles which are either free from each other or joined together to varying degrees. It is generally supposed that *Caltha*, *Trollius* and *Eranthis* are the nearest relatives of *Helleborus* although there is at present no clear answer to this question. Certain chemical evidence, for example the presence of ranunculin, suggests a link with *Ranunculus*, *Anemone* and *Clematis*, whereas using serological techniques, Jensen (1971) showed that *Helleborus* and *Eranthis* had little in common and that *Eranthis* was 'more similar to *Actaea/Cimicifuga*

DISTRIBUTION MAP OF HELLEBORUS SPECIES

Since the exact distribution of each species is not known, the areas shown on the map must be taken as a rough guide only. The numerical sequence is the same as that of the species decribed in the text.

1	*H. vesicarius*	9	*H. torquatus*
2	*H. foetidus* (widespread in W. Europe)	10	*H. atrorubens*
3	*H. argutifolius*	11	*H. dumetorum*
4	*H. lividus*	12	*H. viridis* (widespread in W. Europe)
5	*H. niger*	13	*H. odorus*
6	*H. orientalis*	14	*H. multifidus*
7	*H. cyclophyllus*	15	*H. thibetanus* from China – not shown
8	*H. purpurascens*		

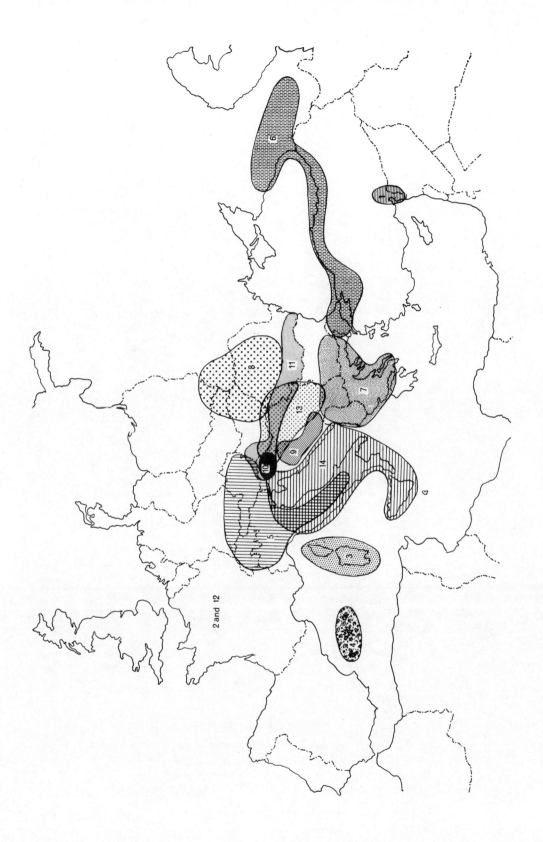

LEAVES OF HELLEBORUS SPECIES

To show shape only; the relative sizes of the drawings are of no significance.

A *H. viridis*
B *H. multifidus* subsp. *hercegovinus*
C *H. odorus*
D *H. thibetanus*

E *H. cyclophyllus*
F *H. dumetorum*
G *H. foetidus*

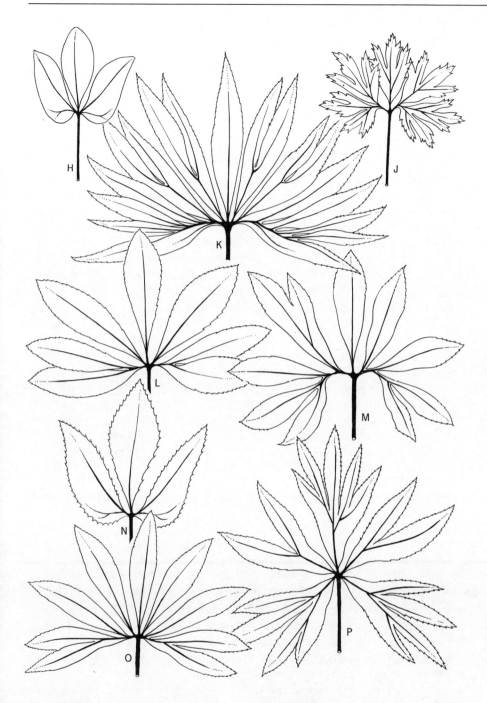

H *H. lividus*
J *H. vesicarius*
K *H. serbicus*
L *H. orientalis*

M *H. niger*
N *H. argutifolius*
O *H. atrorubens*
P *H. purpurascens*

than to *Helleborus*'. He further noted that *Helleborus* showed 'unexpected strong similarities with achene-fruited or annual members of the *Ranunculaceae* (*Myosurus*, *Adonis*, *Consolida*) too'! All things considered it would appear that when searching for the closest relatives of *Helleborus*, the most likely candidates are *Trollius*, *Caltha* and possibly *Eranthis*.

Although the generic name '*Elleborus*' dates back at least to ancient Greek times it is to Linneaus to whom we turn for our presently accepted nomenclature. In 1753 he simplified the varied and often cumbersome systems of naming by proposing a binomial arrangement with a generic name followed by a species epithet. The genus *Helleborus* in the sense of Linnaeus consisted of five species, *H. hyemalis*, *H. niger*, *H. viridis*, *H. foetidus* and *H. trifolius*. The first of these is what we now call *Eranthis hyemalis*, the Winter Aconite, and the last is the North American woodlander known as *Coptis trifolia*. *H. niger*, the name for the Christmas Rose, was not Linnaeus' own for it had appeared in other much earlier works, for example in Clusius' *Rariorum Plantarum Historia* (1601), as *Elleborus niger legitimus*, and in Bauhin's *Pinax Theatri Botanici* (1671) as *Helleborus niger flore roseo*. Undoubtedly the name was a straight translation of '*Elleborus melas*', the Black Hellebore of the ancient Greeks.

Philip Miller in his splendid *Gardeners' Dictionary* of 1768 added one *Helleborus* species to Linnaeus' list, namely *H. trifolius*, referring to the Corsican Hellebore which we now call *H. argutifolius*. Clearly Miller's name, although the oldest one for this species, cannot be used since Linnaeus had already made use of the epithet *trifolius* for a quite different plant (now *Coptis*). *H. lividus* and *H. orientalis* were added to the list of known species in 1789, and the majority were described during the first half of the 19th century. The last distinct species was discovered and named in 1885, *H. thibetanus* from China, and this will also be the last one to be introduced into western gardens. Of course, there are a great many more names in existence than there are actual species, this state of affairs being caused by the great variation to be found in nearly all wild Hellebores but especially in *H. orientalis* and some of the Balkan green- and purple-flowered ones. A botanist who accepts only a small amount of variation within each species will inevitably end up with many more than one which takes a broad view of each.

Few early attempts were made to classify the known species of Hellebore, most of the systems suggested consisting of two groups based on whether or not the leaves and flowers were carried on the same stem, as in *H. foetidus*, or on separate stems like *H. orientalis*. A. Braun and C. Bouché of Berlin Botanic Garden adopted this view in 1861, naming the two groups *Caulescentes*, which housed the leafy-stemmed species *H. lividus* and *H. foetidus*, and *Scapigeri* containing all those species whose leaf and flower stems were produced from the rhizome on separate stems. J.G. Baker of Kew (1877) recognised the same two groups but used the names *Caulescentes* and *Acaules*.

It is clear however that the division of the genus into two such broad groups is unsatisfactory and this fact was recognised as long ago as 1839 when Edouard Spach, in his *Histoire Naturelle des Végétaux*, suggested three sections, (1) *Chionorhodon*, with *H. niger* as the sole representative, (2) *Helleborastrum*, which contained all the known European 'stemless' species such as *H. viridis*, *H. purpurascens*, *H. odorus* and their relatives, and (3) *Griphopus* for the stemmed

H. orientalis, the Lenten Rose

H. niger near Kranjska Gora in
Yugoslavia

H. lividus in cultivation

H. orientalis habitat in N. Turkey

H. orientalis subsp. *abchasicus* near
Sukhumi, USSR. (Photo: J. Whitehead)

H. orientalis near Bolu in N. Turkey

H. purpurascens in Romania, Bucegi Mts.
(Photo: G E Barrett)

H. cyclophyllus near Péc in S. Yugoslavia

H. purpurascens in cultivation

H. cyclophyllus habitat in Yugoslavia.
(Photo: H & M Crook)

species *H. foetidus* and *H. lividus* (incl. *H. argutifolius*).

Dr Victor Schiffner (1889) was the principal monographer of the genus and his concept of the infra-generic classification can largely be accepted as it stands, although it is my opinion that the initial division into the two broad groups mentioned above should be ignored. For the two primary 'splits' in the genus Schiffner chose a combination of names, *Caulescentes* Braun & Bouché and *Acaules* Baker, although there was in fact no case for rejecting Braun's earlier epithet, *Scapigeri* for the latter. Within *Caulescentes* there were three sections, (1) *Syncarpus*, for the unique *H. vesicarius*, (2) *Griphopus*, which this time was restricted to *H. foetidus*, and (3) *Chenopus* for *H. argutifolius* and *H. lividus*. The *Acaules* group consisted of sections (4) *Chionorhodon* for *H. niger* and (5) *Euhelleborus* for the rest of the stemless species, constituting the bulk of the genus.

To summarise, the classification of Schiffner (1889) was as follows:

A. *Hellebori Caulescentes* A. Braun & Bouché
   SECTION ONE   *Syncarpus* Schiffner
   SECTION TWO   *Griphopus* Spach (in part)
   SECTION THREE *Chenopus* Schiffner
B. *Hellebori Acaules* Baker
   SECTION FOUR   *Chionorhodon* Spach
   SECTION FIVE   *Euhelleborus* Schiffner

The next major account of the genus was in 1938 by Prof. E. Ulbrich who largely followed Schiffner, with a few modifications. Again *Helleborus* was divided into two but the *Acaules* group was correctly allotted the oldest available name, *Scapigeri*. A new section, *Dicarpon*, was added for the Chinese species, and the section *Euhelleborus* reverted to Spach's earlier name *Helleborastrum*.

Thus Ulbrich's classification appeared as follows:

Hellebori Caulescentes A. Braun & Bouché
   SECTION ONE   *Syncarpus* Schiffner
   SECTION TWO   *Griphopus* Spach
   SECTION THREE *Chenopus* Schiffner
Hellebori Scapigeri A. Braun & Bouché
   SECTION FOUR   *Chionorhodon* Spach
   SECTION FIVE   *Dicarpon* Ulbrich
   SECTION SIX   *Helleborastrum* Spach

G. Hegi, *Illustrierte Flora von Mittel-Europa* (1974) follows this classification but in order to comply with modern nomenclatural practice, changes the name of sect. *Chionorhodon* to sect. *Helleborus*, since this section contains the type species of the genus, *H. niger*. There is unfortunately a serious error in this work in that the two major groups have been interchanged, the stemmed species, *H. foetidus* and *H. lividus*, being attributed to the *Scapigeri* (*Acaules*) group and all the so-called stemless Hellebores to the *Caulescent* group!

Taking into account as many different factors as are at present available it seems to me that, as I have said above, it is incorrect to divide the genus into two broad groups based on the absence or presence of basal leaves. The general structure of the plants, the ability (or not) of the species to hybridise, the morphology of the pollen grains and the characteristics of the seeds lead me to believe that a more natural classification may be presented by dividing the genus directly into six sections with no intervening groups (for a key to these sections, see page 44):

Genus Helleborus
SECTION ONE	*Syncarpus* Schiffner
SECTION TWO	*Griphopus* Spach
SECTION THREE	*Chenopus* Schiffner
SECTION FOUR	*Helleborus*
SECTION FIVE	*Helleborastrum* Spach
SECTION SIX	*Dicarpon* Ulbrich

The pollen studies of Nowicke & Skvarla (1983) largely support this view. *H. niger* (sect. *Helleborus*) has different pollen morphology from that of all the other species in that there is no reticulate pattern on the surface. The species of sect. *Helleborastrum* are also distinct with their coarsely reticulate pollen grains, leaving *H. foetidus*, *H. lividus*, *H. argutifolius*, *H. vesicarius* and *H. thibetanus*, all of which have finely reticulate pollen. *H. thibetanus* of sect. *Dicarpon*, although similar in most respects to the species of sect. *Helleborastrum*, possesses pollen more like that of *H. foetidus* and *H. lividus*, so the view that it should be given a section of its own is somewhat strengthened. *H. vesicarius* also has a slightly different surface architecture on its pollen grains so can be recognised as constituting a separate section, especially in view of all the other major differences. *H. foetidus*, although having similar pollen to that of *H. lividus* and *H. argutifolius*, is so distinct in other ways that it is also best separated at sectional level from them.

Hybridisation between sections and within sections

Although more hybridisation experiments are required, the currently available information suggests that the division of *Helleborus* into these six sections is correct.

Section *Syncarpus*. Ability to hybridise unknown.

Section *Griphopus*. The one species (*H. foetidus*) will cross with sect. *Chenopus* producing sterile offspring. Also two unconfirmed reports of hybrids with sect. *Helleborastrum* (see page 145).

Section *Chenopus*. The two species represented (*H. argutifolius* and *H. lividus*) will cross with sect. *Helleborus* and one of them has been hybridised with sect. *Griphopus*; in all cases the offspring are sterile. Within sect. *Chenopus* the two species hybridise giving fertile offspring.

Section *Helleborus*. The one species (*H. niger*) will cross with sect. *Chenopus*, producing sterile offspring.

Section *Helleborastrum*. The nine species contained in this, the largest section, all appear to hybridise with each other producing fertile offspring. There are only two reports of inter-section crosses, (1) with sect. *Helleborus* (see page 146), involving *H. niger* and *H. viridis*, and (2) unconfirmed natural hybrids between *H. viridis* (sect. *Helleborastrum*) and *H. foetidus* (sect. *Griphopus*) (see page 145).

Section *Dicarpon*. Ability to hybridise unknown.

5

The Structure of Hellebores

Rhizomatous perennial herbs, either producing long-stalked basal leaves and separate non-leafy flower stems (but furnished with bracts which may be leaf-like), or producing tough 'woody' stems carrying leaves and terminal inflorescences.

Rootstock. The majority of species have well-developed horizontal rhizomes with sympodial branching, producing fairly thick roots which are more or less unbranched in the upper part and much branched towards the tips, brown at first becoming blackish. *H. foetidus*, however, has a poorly developed rhizome, usually obliquely upright and the transition from this into the aerial stem is gradual and ill-defined. (see page 147)

RHIZOMES OF HELLEBORES

Left *H. foetidus* in which the poorly developed rhizome merges into the aerial stem. Right *H. orientalis*, showing a stout rhizome, typical of most of the species.

Stems. The stem bases are enclosed by 2 or 3 short papery sheaths. Most species have basal leaves and leafless flower stems bearing bracts which subtend the branches of the inflorescence and the flowers; these bracts may be entire, or divided so that they resemble reduced leaves. *H. lividus*, *H. argutifolius* and *H. foetidus* have overwintering semi-woody stems which are replaced annually after flowering; these bear the leaves, the flowers, and their associated bracts, and are usually fairly thin at ground level, becoming thicker towards the apex. *H. vesicarius* has both basal leaves and stem leaves.

Leaves. Hellebore leaves are mostly pedately divided with five or more segments (see drawings, pages 30 and 31); in some species (e.g. *H. viridis*) they are sometimes weakly pedate, inclining to palmate (digitate); in *H. purpurascens* they are almost strictly palmate. *H. argutifolius*, *H. lividus* and *H. vesicarius* have 3-lobed leaves. In most species the leaflets are coarsely toothed, sometimes spiny-toothed (*H. argutifolius*) and rarely (*H. lividus*) entire-margined. The texture is often leathery and the venation conspicuous and prominent on the underside. In some species they are entirely glabrous, in others pubescent on the underside, usually on the veins but occasionally all over. The majority of species die down in the winter but *H. orientalis* and *H. odorus* have overwintering basal leaves, and in *H. argutifolius*, *H. lividus* and *H. foetidus* the stems and their leaves are present in winter. *H. vesicarius* is winter-green and dies down in summer.

Inflorescence. Hellebores have loosely branched cymes of flowers, mostly rather few-flowered (up to 7 flowers) but *H. foetidus* and *H. argutifolius* have larger many-flowered paniculate cymes. In *H. niger* the inflorescences may be reduced to a solitary flower, and sometimes also in weak-growing plants of other species.

Bracts. These vary from entire and untoothed (e.g. *H. niger*) to divided and leaf-like with coarse teeth; the lowest ones, subtending the branches, are the largest and most divided, reducing in size upwards to those subtending the flowers which are usually less divided and more finely toothed.

Flowers. Pendent in varying degrees, or facing outwards horizontally, flattish to bell-shaped. They are bisexual, regular in shape with their parts spirally arranged. The outer whorl consists of 5 large, usually overlapping perianth segments (sepals) which may be white, green or purple, or some combination of these colours, turning green after anthesis and continuing to assist in photosynthesis, persisting through into the fruiting stage. The inner whorl (equivalent to petals) consists of up to 32 small green or occasionally dark purple tubular or funnel-shaped, shortly stalked, nectaries ('nectar petals', 'honey leaves').

Stamens. Numerous, very variable in number (approximately 35–125) with slender filaments which are erect at first, elongating and arching outwards as they mature; anthers elliptical or oblong, yellow or cream.

Pollen. *Helleborus* pollen is 3-colpate (i.e. has 3 apertures) and is rather distinct from that of most other genera in the Ranunculaceae in having a surface which is not covered with minute spines. The outer surface (tectum), as seen through a

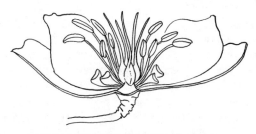

SECTION OF HELLEBORE FLOWER

Flower parts shown, working from the outside into the centre: Perianth segments; smaller funnel-shaped nectaries; stamens; pistils, each consisting of ovary and style with terminal stigma.

scanning electron microscope, is colliculate (like a cobbled road) with a finely to coarsely reticulate pattern of depressions. In *H. niger* there are only a few of these 'holes' so there is no obvious reticulate pattern, the surface appearing almost unbroken (apart from the 3 long colpi). In *H. foetidus, H. lividus, H. argutifolius, H. vesicarius* and *H. thibetanus* the tectum is finely reticulate, and in the rest of the species rather more coarsely reticulate. [Information largely from Nowicke & Skvarla (1983)]

Pollination. The flowers are protogynous, that is the stigmas reach maturity before the stamens so that cross-pollination is encouraged; however, by the later stages of flowering, self-pollination is possible. The pollinating agents are usually bees of the genera *Apis* (Honey bees), *Bombus* (Bumble bees) and *Anthophora* (Flower bees). A few *Helleborus* species have strongly scented flowers, apparently the scent being most intense in the nectaries. The sepals of some of the species have been shown to have a medium to high ultra-violet reflection whereas the nectaries were found to be UV free; presumably the bees are attracted initially by the sepals and, having landed, then find the scented nectaries.

Carpels 2–10, sessile, free from each other or slightly fused at the base, containing numerous ovules; styles usually stout, straight or curved; stigmas punctiform (dot-like). (see page 147)

Fruit. A group of 2-8 several-seeded follicles, united at the base or free, usually dehiscent but *H. vesicarius* has much-inflated follicles which are indehiscent. (see page 30)

Seeds. Oblong or nearly spherical with a small ridge on one side, sometimes provided with an enlarged fleshy whitish ridge (elaiosome or 'oil body'). (see page 30)

Seed dispersal. Ants are known to distribute seeds (myrmecochory), attracted to the elaiosome which has been shown to contain sugars, fats and vitamin C; this is particularly well-developed in *H. niger, H. foetidus, H. argutifolius* and *H. lividus.* Snails have also been observed acting as dispersal agents with seed sticking to their bodies. In *H. vesicarius* the follicles are indehiscent and are fused together into a balloon-like structure at maturity; the pedicel breaks allowing the whole fruit to fall and to be blown along by the wind, in time breaking up and scattering the seeds.

Germination. This usually takes place in autumn or winter. At first, 2 undivided, untoothed cotyledons are produced above ground (see drawing, below), sometimes with the seed coat still attached to one of them. The shape is ovate or oblong, narrowing gradually at the base into the stem (hypocotyl). In all species except *H. vesicarius* there is a growing point between the cotyledons which soon gives rise to the first foliage leaf. This is either undivided (*H. lividus* and *H. argutifolius*) or divided, usually into 3 leaflets (all other species except *H. vesicarius*). *H. vesicarius* produces only 2 large obovate cotyledons in its first year with no true leaves, the seedling appearing to be 'blind'. After a summer dormancy the true foliage leaves are produced from a bud below ground on the young rhizome.

SEEDLINGS OF HELLEBORES

Each seedling shows two cotyledons or seed leaves. Left to right: *H. orientalis*, *H. argutifolius*, *H. foetidus* and *H. vesicarius*, which produces no true leaves between the cotyledons.

Cytology. All the chromosome counts published to date are $2n = 32$ and the plants are thought to represent tetraploids with a basic number of 8. However, a thorough cytological survey of the genus is needed since it may give an indication as to the validity or otherwise of the sectional classification. Clearly such a survey will have to be based on plants of known wild source since garden material is frequently of hybrid origin.

Habitats. Habitat details are given for each species but in general Hellebores are plants of deciduous woodland and scrub, although they sometimes occur in open grassland or rocky places at higher altitudes. They are usually associated with limestone or chalk formations but *H. orientalis* is frequently found in situations where Rhododendrons occur. *H. vesicarius* grows in rocky places which become sun-baked in summer.

6

Classification of the genus *Helleborus* Linn.

There are six Sections defined as follows:

SECTION 1 *Syncarpus* Schiffner
  Plant with both basal leaves and cauline leaves, dying down completely in summer. Leaves with 3(–5) coarsely jagged leaflets. Bracts divided and leaf-like. Flowers bell-shaped, green with a brownish apex to segments. Pollen with a finely reticulate surface. Follicles usually 3, grossly inflated in fruit and joined together for half of their length. Seeds nearly spherical, with no swollen appendage.
  Species: *H. vesicarius.*

SECTION 2. *Griphopus* Spach
  Plant evergreen with sub-shrubby stems bearing cauline leaves; basal leaves absent. Leaves pedate with 7–10 narrow leaflets. Bracts entire (at least the upper ones). Flowers bell-shaped, green with a brownish apex to segments. Pollen surface finely reticulate. Follicles usually 3, not grossly inflated, joined at base only. Seeds oblong with a fleshy appendage.
  Species: *H. foetidus.*

SECTION 3. *Chenopus* Schiffner
  Plant evergreen with sub-shrubby stems bearing cauline leaves; basal leaves absent. Leaves with 3 leaflets. Bracts entire (at least the upper ones). Flowers cup- or bowl-shaped, wholly green or suffused pinkish-purple. Pollen surface finely reticulate. Follicles usually 3–6, not grossly inflated. Seeds oblong with a fleshy whitish appendage.
  Species: *H. argutifolius, H. lividus.*

SECTION 4. *Helleborus*
  Plant with basal leaves only; cauline leaves absent (but bracts present on flower stems). Leaves overwintering, pedate with 7–9 leaflets. Bracts entire. Flowers flattish, white (often ageing pinkish). Pollen surface with no reticulate pattern. Follicles usually 5–8, not grossly inflated. Seeds oblong with a large whitish elaiosome.
  Species: *H. niger*

SECTION 5. *Helleborastrum* Spach

Plant with basal leaves only; cauline leaves absent (but bracts present on flower stems). Leaves winter-deciduous or overwintering, usually pedate with 7–many leaflets. Bracts divided and leaf-like but reduced in size. Flowers usually saucer-shaped or shallowly cup-shaped, green, purple, violet or creamy-white, sometimes spotted internally. Pollen surface with a coarsely reticulate pattern. Follicles usually 4–7, not grossly inflated. Seeds oblong with a small ridge on one side.

Species: *H. orientalis, H. cyclophyllus, H. purpurascens, H. torquatus, H. atrorubens, H. dumetorum, H. viridis, H. odorus, H. multifidus.*

SECTION 6. *Dicarpon* Ulbrich

Plant with basal leaves only; cauline leaves absent (but bracts present on flower stems). Leaves winter-deciduous, pedate with 7–10 segments. Bracts divided and leaf-like but reduced in size. Flowers ?saucer-shaped, pink or red. Pollen surface with a finely reticulate pattern. Follicles usually 2, not grossly inflated. Seeds oblong with a small ridge on one side.

Species: *H. thibetanus.*

Key to the Sections of Helleborus

1a. Plant dying down completely in summer. Follicles very large and inflated .... SECTION 1. *Syncarpus*

b. Plant not dying down in summer. Follicles not greatly expanded 2

2a. Leaves and flowers produced all on the same stem, with no basal leaves present 3

b. Leaves basal, produced on separate stems from the flowers 4

3a. Leaves with 3 broad leaflets .... SECTION 3. *Chenopus*

b. Leaves with 7–10 narrow leaflets .... SECTION 2. *Griphopus*

4a. Bracts undivided; flowers white, 4.5–11 cm diameter; seeds with an enlarged fleshy elaiosome; pollen surface more or less continuous, not perforated–reticulate....................................... SECTION 4. *Helleborus*

b. Bracts divided and toothed; flowers variously coloured but if white, usually not more than 7 cm diameter; seeds with a thin ridge; pollen surface perforated into a reticulate pattern 5

5a. Carpels 2, rarely 3, but normally only 2 developing into follicles; pollen with finely reticulate tectum (surface).................. SECTION 6. *Dicarpon*

b. Carpels 3 or more; pollen with coarsely reticulate tectum ....SECTION 5. *Helleborastrum*

H. torquatus, a deep blackish-purple form growing in S. Yugoslavia.
(Photo: H & M Crook)

H. torquatus near Kolašin, S. Yugoslavia

H. torquatus, a paler, dove-coloured form from Plav, S. Yugoslavia

H. torquatus, a double form found by Miss E. Strangman in W. Yugoslavia

H. foetidus, the Stinking Hellebore

Key to the species of Helleborus

N.B. *On garden plants this key may not produce a clear result,*
since many cultivars are of hybrid origin

1a. Plant dying down in summer; seed pods much-inflated; leaves soft in texture with 3(–5) coarsely jagged leaflets .... 1. *H. vesicarius*

b. Plants remaining in growth in summer; seed pods not grossly inflated; leaves mostly with more than 3 leaflets but if with 3 then not with jagged margins (may be spiny-toothed) and leathery in texture 2

2a. Basal leaves absent, the leaves and flowers carried on the same rather woody stem 3

b. Basal leaves present, carried on stems separate from those of the flowers, although the flower stems may bear reduced leaf-like bracts.................. 5

3a. Leaves with 7–10 rather narrow leaflets .... 2. *H. foetidus*

b. Leaves with 3 rather broad leaflets.. 4

4a. Leaves plain green with spiny-toothed margins; plant up to 1.2 m in height; flowers green............................... 3. *H. argutifolius* (*H. corsicus*)

b. Leaves suffused pinkish-purple beneath, dark green with creamy veins above, margin smooth or with a few widely spaced teeth; plant up to 45 cm in height; flowers green suffused pinkish-purple .... 4. *H. lividus*

5a. Bracts (or 'cauline leaves') not toothed or divided; flowers white, 4.5–11 cm diameter.. 5. *H. niger*

b. Bracts (or 'cauline leaves') toothed and with leaf-like divisions; flowers variously coloured, including white, but if white then usually with a greenish suffusion, and not more than 7 cm diameter............................ 6

6a. Carpels free from each other right to the base; plant with leathery overwintering leaves and large white or purple flowers, *or* with winter-deciduous leaves and large green flowers (5–7 cm diam.) 7

b. Carpels shortly joined together at the base (for up to 5 mm); plant with either winter-deciduous leaves and purple or small green flowers 2.5–5 cm diam.) *or* with overwintering leaves, and large green flowers (5–7 cm diam.)... 8

7a. Flowers green, scented; leaves densely silvery-hairy on the underside when young, not normally overwintering .... 7. *H. cyclophyllus*

b. Flowers white or in various shades of purple, pinkish-purple or purple-spotted, unscented; leaves hairless or sparsely hairy on the underside, overwintering.. 6. *H. orientalis*
(incl. *H. abchasicus* & *H. guttatus*)

8a. Flowers in various shades of purple, violet or pink, at least on the exterior of the perianth segments 9

The species of *Helleborus*

SECTION ONE

Syncarpus

1 *Helleborus vesicarius*

The specific name of this unusual Hellebore means bladder-like and refers to the extraordinary inflated seed heads (follicles) which at maturity are nearly spherical in outline and up to 7.5 cm across. A large clump furnished with many of these pale yellowish green bladders is a remarkable sight and in this state would be an excellent feature in the garden if it were easier to achieve, but to date the species has proved somewhat reluctant to perform impressively.

In fact it is in fruit that *H. vesicarius* is at its most striking and without this feature it would, as a garden plant, have little to recommend it other than botanical curiosity and rarity. The pendent bell-shaped flowers are small and green with brownish tips, rather like those of the better known *H. foetidus*, but there the similarity ends for *H. vesicarius* has bright fresh green leaves which are basically divided into three leaflets; each of these is deeply and irregularly cut into coarse acute lobes, quite unlike the pedate dark green serrate-edged ones of *H. foetidus*.

H. vesicarius is unique in the genus in several ways, quite apart from having the bladder-like fruits and distinctive leaves. Firstly, the cycle of growth is unlike that of any other species, the plant being summer-dormant rather than dying down in winter, and secondly the foliage consists of both basal leaves and stem leaves whereas all the rest of the species can be divided into those with stem leaves or without. In the fruiting stage the three follicles are fused together for about half their length and the large seeds which they contain are almost spherical, again characters which are not encountered in any other species. Dr V. Schiffner (1889) expressed this uniqueness by placing it in a separate section, Syncarpus, which refers to the joined carpels (follicles) and it is best to continue to treat it in this way for it does not readily fall into any of the other groupings. In their palynological study of *Helleborus*, Nowicke & Skvarla (1983) found that the pollen of *H. vesicarius* possessed a finely reticulate tectum so in this way it is rather similar to *H. argutifolius* and *H. foetidus* but nevertheless it was considered sufficiently distinct for them to note that 'pollen morphology would support the separate sectional status of *H. vesicarius*'.

This curious Hellebore occurs wild in a limited area of southern Turkey and northern Syria, mainly in the Amanus mountains and adjacent regions, where it receives rainfall in autumn, winter and spring followed by a long dry and warm summer. In growth pattern it behaves in a similar way to the many bulbous plants which occur in the region and copes with this climate by making its main growth in the damp part of the year commencing in autumn then dying down to a resting crown in summer after fruiting in May and June. The strong fleshy roots act as a storage system during this adverse period although they do also penetrate deeply enough into the heavy soil to be in contact with a certain amount of moisture. Its habitat is in clearings in sparse dryish woodland or scrub which often consists largely of deciduous Oak, at altitudes of 500–1500 metres in a clay soil between limestone outcrops. There is very little humus content in the soil except for a surface mulch of decaying leaves and other herbaceous vegetation. Ole Sønderhousen tested the soil in one area and found it to have a pH of 7.85 so, in the wild at least, the species shows a marked preference for alkaline conditions. Other interesting garden-worthy plants occurring in the same area are *Acanthus syriacus*, *Arum dioscoridis*, *Hyacinthus orientalis*, *Cyclamen coum* and several species of *Iris*, *Crocus*, and *Fritillaria*.

In the fruiting stage, usually in May or June, when the large inflated follicles are ripe, the whole fruiting head breaks off and, being light and nearly spherical, is dispersed by the wind eventually breaking up irregularly rather than remaining attached to the plant and splitting open as in other Hellebores. It is in fact a type of 'tumbleweed' and Ulbrich used the vernacular name 'Wind Blown Hellebore' for this species. This is not an uncommon method of dispersal in dry steppe-type habitats.

Although not a very widespread species, the future of *H. vesicarius* appears to be fairly safe since it grows in rocky hilly terrain which is unlikely to be taken over as farm land, or used for building. It is also a fairly difficult plant to dig up and transplant so is relatively safe from collectors, and in any case its horticultural appeal is very limited, mainly to Hellebore enthusiasts.

Cultivation

As might be expected of a plant from a relatively mild district of southern Turkey, *H. vesicarius* is not as hardy as those species from further north and does not thrive in the open garden in areas where the soil freezes to a great depth. Nevertheless, I have grown it outside in Surrey for several years and, in spite of its foliage sometimes being frozen rigid in the winter, it has survived unscathed. The clue to success, as with so many plants, is in choosing a good site where it receives some degree of protection from neighbouring plants. Before considering the position in which to plant it let us just remind ourselves that, although it grows in a region which is hot and dry in summer, the roots penetrate deeply enough to find moisture. Thus, I would not recommend drying out completely a plant growing in a pot since it would almost certainly desiccate and die. In the autumn months rain comes to southern Turkey and this is when *H. vesicarius* begins to grow, showing root activity and often some aerial growth as well. The main leaf growth and the appearance of flower stems takes place in spring when there is warm sun and a good supply of moisture still available in the soil but by early summer most plants will have completed their growth and are preparing to die down for the next four or five months. This cycle of growth resembles that of most Mediterranean bulbous plants and indeed *H. vesicarius* can be more or less treated as a bulb except that it cannot be dug up and dried! It can be cultivated very satisfactorily if planted out into a bulb frame where it can be left undisturbed and given its winter moisture and summer warmth; it associates particularly well with Irises of the Oncocyclus group which require very similar treatment. It may also be grown in a large deep pot of gritty compost in a cool greenhouse (just frost-free) but will require feeding during its period of growth and should preferably be plunged into sand during summer so that the roots do not become too hot and dry. If outdoor cultivation is contemplated then a fairly sunny position should be chosen with some protection from the north and east, and a site where it will become drier during its summer dormancy. The key to this drying out is to plant it near to a shrub whose roots will use up any excess moisture in summer. My own experimental planting was fairly successful on the south side of a clump of lavender in a sandy soil where it received protection in winter and became fairly dry and warm in summer, although the roots delved down into heavy clay below a sand bed which I had made up for bulbs. I have heard of others who have grown it successfully at the base of a beech hedge where the same set of factors are to be found. It is probably best to choose deciduous shrubby companions so that there is some protection in winter and spring but not too much shade or competition for moisture while the Hellebore is in growth, whereas in summer when the shrubs are in leaf any excess water is used up, leaving it relatively dry for its dormant period. I doubt that planting at the base of a coniferous hedge would work so well since the soil in these sites is usually very dry and starved throughout the year. Certainly in the wild *H. vesicarius* is mainly associated with deciduous scrub.

Propagation in cultivation is almost entirely by seed for although division is possible in late summer before growth begins it is unlikely that anyone with a decent plant of this rare species would contemplate digging it up and cutting it into pieces! Seeds are sometimes produced by individual plants but fruiting is more reliable if there are at least two, cross-pollinated by hand several times during the flowering period to make sure of fertilization. Seeds appear to germinate well during autumn or winter, but the pots should be kept for at least three years since seedlings are likely to appear spasmodically rather than all at one time. It thus appears that they retain their viability longer than those of most Hellebores. This is what one would expect of a plant from rather hot dry places where seeds lie dormant and dry for several months before the opportunity arises for them to germinate.

On germination two large cotyledons are produced at the top of a false stem and in my experience this is all that happens during the first growing season, with no true leaves appearing between the cotyledons as in other Hellebore species, so that they appear to be 'blind'. In summer these cotyledons die down to a resting crown which on starting into growth the next autumn produces normal, but small, basal leaves. When mature enough to flower, cauline leaves on the flower stem as well as basal leaves are produced, this taking about four or five years from germination.

H. vesicarius Aucher in Ann. Sci. Nat. 16: 357 (1841).

Type: Turkey, Antakya (Hatay) Province, Akra Dağ (Mt. Cassius), *Aucher* 60
(specimen at Kew)

Description
Herbaceous perennial up to 60 cm in height, dying down completely in summer after fruiting. Rhizome tough, with thick wiry roots. Basal leaves glabrous, thin in texture, bright green, with long petioles 8–25 cm long which are expanded with

wide membranous margins at the base; leaf blade pedate with three primary divisions, the two lateral leaflets sometimes shallowly divided into two. Each leaflet is cut into several jagged teeth which are wedge-shaped at the base and coarsely toothed at the apex, the teeth and terminal lobe acute; the whole leaf may be up to 8 cm long and 15 cm wide; cauline leaves similar but smaller and stalkless or with a short widely winged petiole, glabrous or sometimes slightly pubescent in the young stages. Inflorescence consisting of a loose cyme, each branch of which is subtended by a leaf-like bract divided into three lobes and coarsely toothed; pedicels slender and drooping, sparsely pubescent, 1–2.5 cm long, elongating slightly in fruit. Flowers erect at first becoming pendent, green suffused with a purple or brownish stain towards the apex, sometimes in a band just below the apex, sometimes the whole apical half is coloured, unscented (?always), bell-shaped, about 1.5–2 cm long, 1.5–1.7 cm wide; sepals nearly equal but the two outer ones usually slightly smaller than the three inner ones, obovate or elliptic, rounded or sometimes truncate (squared) or emarginate at the apex, 1.5–2 cm long, 0.8–1.5 cm wide; nectaries about 5, curved-tubular with an oblique mouth and reflexed lip, 7–8 mm long, shortly stalked; stamens numerous, erect, slightly shorter than the sepals, anthers oval, 1.5–2 mm long; carpels 3, fused for about a third of their length; styles about equalling or slightly shorter than the stamens. Follicles much-expanded and inflated when ripe, fused for about half their length and forming an almost globose 3-winged fruit up to 7.5 cm long, pale yellowish green with a conspicuous reticulate pattern of veins. The fruit is indehiscent, falling in its entirety with the sepals still attached, and is wind-dispersed, breaking up irregularly to scatter the seeds; seeds 3–6 in each follicle, broadly ellipsoid or nearly spherical, about 3–5 mm long, rugose, with a low ridge along one side.

Flowering period (March–)April–May in the wild, February–March in cultivation.

Habitat Rocky hillsides in mainly deciduous Oak scrub or dryish areas in turf with other herbaceous plants, on limestone formations, 550–1500 metres.

Distribution S. Turkey, in the vilayets (provinces) of Antakya (Hatay), Maraş, Gaziantep & Adana (Seyhan); adjacent N. Syria.

SECTION TWO

Griphopus

2 *Helleborus foetidus*

One would imagine, by the range of derogatory vernacular names bestowed upon this poor plant, that it was scarcely worth allowing near the garden! Stinking Hellebore, Dungweed, Stinkwort, Läusekraut and Stinkende Niesswurz are merely a selection of the least flattering, but Setterwort and Bear's Foot are perhaps slightly more euphonius, the last presumably referring to the narrow claw-like leaflets. However, the plant is not devastatingly malodorous, certainly no worse than many other plants, and some forms, in fact, have sweetly scented flowers. The unpleasant smell is released mainly when the foliage is being handled and is really not at all noticeable under normal circumstances, so that this harsh criticism of the species is scarcely justified. *H. foetidus* is, on the contrary, a splendid garden plant, a tough evergreen with attractively divided deep green leaves making fine rather stately plants which are a welcome sight in midwinter when the shoots are crowned by the young inflorescences with their large pale green bracts. This display usually begins before Christmas, the flowers then opening early in the New Year and continuing until February or March.

Like *H. argutifolius* and *H. lividus*, *H. foetidus* is a member of the caulescent group, having no basal leaves but instead a tough woody stem carrying many stem leaves and a terminal inflorescence. This stem is of annual duration, dying away after fruiting to be replaced by one or more new ones for the next season. A very vigorous plant may have up to six separate stems forming a large mound of growth as much as a metre across and 80 cm in height but in the wild they often remain with single stems. In all stages of growth it is a very easy Hellebore to recognise, firstly on account of its stemmed growth habit and secondly because of its much-divided leaves with narrow leaflets; the other caulescent species have leaves consisting of three wide leaflets. It is however quite obvious that the pedate leaf of *H. foetidus* is fundamentally three-parted, the centre leaflet undivided and the two lateral ones deeply subdivided into several narrow lobes (see page 30). In the flowering stage it is equally easy to recognise *H. foetidus* with its small, almost globular or bell-shaped green flowers rimmed with brown or purple; the only other species with flowers of a similar shape and size is the Turkish *H. vesicarius* but this is very different in many other ways and there is little need for further comparison. *H. vesicarius* is clearly distinct from all other species and was placed by Schiffner in a section of its own, a course followed by most later authors. *H. foetidus* is not such a clear-cut case although Schiffner also regarded it as sufficiently distinct to merit a monotypic section called Griphopus. In their pollen study of the genus, Joan Nowicke and John Skvarla (1983) showed that *H. foetidus* and *H. lividus* were very similar and made the comment that 'although pollen morphology suggests that these two species are closely related, leaf morphology and geographical distribution would support their treatment in monotypic sections as established by Schiffner'.

There are, to my knowledge, no hybrids of *H. foetidus* in cultivation and it appears to be reluctant to cross with any other species. The only record that I know of was reported to me (personal communication) by Tony Venison who, when travelling with Richard Gorer, Anthony Huxley and Ivor Barton in northern Spain, saw an area 'between Soria and Logrono where populations of *H. foetidus* and *H. viridis* overlapped and there were many apparent hybrids'.

Although always instantly recognisable, *H. foetidus* does vary considerably in its features and as garden plants some variants are better than others. Particularly strong-growing, very floriferous forms seem to occur in parts of southern Europe and one of these is occasionally encountered in gardens as 'Italian Form'. I have already mentioned that plants with fragrant flowers have been found and these too are around in cultivation. One such selection, which has been christened 'Miss Jekyll's Scented Form' has, apart from the fragrance, green flowers lacking any brown colouration. It seems that particularly strongly scented forms occur in southern Spain. Other variants have also been selected and one of the best of these has been named 'Wester Flisk' after a village on the Firth of Tay near Newburgh in Fifeshire, Scotland. This is a delightful plant with rhubarb-red stems and petioles, the stain spreading up to the base of the leaflets and along the branches of the inflorescence; the bracts and flowers, however, retain their pale green colour, contrasting well with this red pigmentation, while the leaves have a greyish green, almost lead-like, appearance. When grown together with 'ordinary' *H. foetidus*, cross-pollination occurs and these features can become somewhat less pronounced in the seedlings.

Occasional mutants of *H. foetidus* occur in which the leaflets are more divided than normal and the marginal teeth so coarse as to almost touch the midrib. These 'laciniate forms' are not attractive and may even possibly be the result of a virus infection.

H. foetidus is a widespread plant in central and western Europe, usually occurring in wooded areas on chalk or limestone formations, although it has also been seen on sandy-gravelly soils. In mainland Europe it is recorded from France, Belgium, Germany, Luxemburg, Austria, Switzerland, Italy, Spain and Portugal, but reports from northern Yugoslavia are not authenticated so that it appears not to extend in an easterly or south-easterly direction beyond Austria, nor does it reach as far north as Scandinavia. The most northern part of its distribution is in Britain where its exact native range is difficult to ascertain since it is frequently cultivated and easily becomes naturalised. It is in fact recorded in most counties of England, southern Scotland and Wales but is absent from Ireland, although garden escapes have been found in several places. Alastair Fitter, in his *Atlas of the Wild Flowers of Britain and Northern Europe*, indicates that it is considered to be naturalised in much of Britain. The main native areas are given as the chalk and limestone regions of the south, i.e. the Downs through to the Cotswolds, but it is almost certainly native in various places as far north as Lancashire and Yorkshire. The records in Scotland, which cover areas as far north as Aberdeen, are thought to refer to garden escapes. In the Mediterranean region, *H. foetidus* is found on the islands of Sicily, Corsica, Sardinia, Majorca and Menorca, thus overlapping in distribution the two much more restricted species *H. argutifolius* and *H. lividus.*

As a medicinal plant *H. foetidus* has been used in the past as a lice deterrent, either as dried powdered roots or as an infusion of the leaves. It is however particularly poisonous to animals and humans and there were considerable risks in using it for this purpose. I can vouch for the efficacy of it as a poison, since one of the more unattractive jobs I have had as a botanist was to poke about in the contents of a dead cow's stomach to ascertain what herbage was contained therein, expecting to find Yew clippings but locating instead the unmistakable leaves of the Stinking (especially on this occasion!) Hellebore. The name Setterwort refers to the curious veterinary practice which I have dealt with on page 26.

Cultivation
H. foetidus is one of the easiest species to cultivate and will reach flowering size in only two or three years from seed. It grows at its strongest in partial shade in a soil which is well supplied with humus, becoming rather feeble in dry situations. There is certainly a preference for alkaline or neutral soils but it can also be cultivated successfully in acid sandy soils if plenty of organic material is incorporated. Seeds are produced with great freedom and these often germinate prolifically near the parent plants, although they are also distributed by ants over a wider area. In view of this easy method of propagation it is not normally necessary to resort to division of the rhizome although this is possible if a particularly desirable form is found which will not breed true from seed. It appears however that the selected fragrant forms and 'Wester Flisk' come reasonably true to type as long as they are not growing alongside 'ordinary' forms where they can be cross-pollinated by insects. Obviously it is necessary to take steps to prevent this if pure stocks are required.

H. foetidus Linn., Sp. Pl. ed. 1: 558 (1753).
Type: 'Habitat in Germania, Helvetica, Gallia' (Linnean Society Herbarium, London)

Synonyms
Helleboraster foetidus (L.) Moench, Meth.: 236 (1794)
Helleborus nemoralis Jord. & Fourr. in Ann. Soc. Linn. Lyon, N.S. 16: 325 (1868)
H. beugesiacus Jord. & Fourr., loc. cit.
H. deflexifolius Jord. & Fourr., loc. cit.
H. rhodanicus Jord. & Fourr., loc. cit.

Description
Glabrous perennial herb up to 80 cm in height with a weakly developed rhizome giving rise to erect leafy green or purplish stems which increase in thickness from ground level upwards; these are of annual duration but are present in winter, dying away after fruiting to be replaced by new ones. Basal leaves absent. Leaves leathery, long-petiolate, all borne on the stem, clustered near the apex but in spring overtopped by the inflorescence, pedate with 7–10 segments, the central

leaflet entire, the lateral ones much-divided; petioles green or strongly stained purplish-red, up to 20 cm long, expanded at the base into a broad sheath clasping the stem; leaf segments narrowly lanceolate or narrowly elliptic, acute at the apex, gradually tapered to the base, up to 20 cm long and up to 2.8 cm wide, usually deep green but occasionally greyish-green; margins serrate, usually conspicuously and coarsely so but sometimes almost entire. Inflorescence consisting of large terminal many-flowered cymes, the whole cluster up to 30 cm across; bracts large and conspicuous, pale yellowish-green, the lower ones elliptic or ovate, often with small leaf-like divisions at the apex, the upper ones ovate, acute, entire; pedicels 1–4.5 cm long. Flowers pendent, green, often suffused with purple-brown towards the apex, unscented or fragrant, bell-shaped, about 1.5–2 cm long, 1.5–2.5 cm in diameter; perianth segments nearly equal, broadly obovate, truncate, emarginate or rounded, 1.5–2 cm long, 1–2 cm wide; nectaries 8–12, shortly stalked, tubular, truncate with an irregularly toothed apex; stamens numerous, erect, equalling or slightly shorter than the sepals; anthers elliptical, about 1.5–2 mm long; carpels normally 3, fused at the base; styles shorter than or equalling the stamens. Follicles leathery when ripe, 2–2.5 cm long (excluding the persistent style), exceeding the tepals; seeds abut 4 mm long, dark brown with a fleshy whitish elaiosome ('oil body').

Flowering time (December–)January–June.

Habitat Woods and scrub, usually on calcareous soils, sea level to 2135 metres.

Distribution Central and western Europe from Austria to Portugal and north to Britain and northern Germany.

SECTION THREE

Chenopus

3 *Helleborus argutifolius*

This well known species, the Corsican Hellebore, is frequently found in literature and catalogues under the more euphonious but incorrect name of *H. corsicus*. It is unfortunate that this epithet was not validly published in accordance with the International Rules of Botanical Nomenclature, being merely listed without a description in the catalogue of the Berlin Botanic Garden in 1813. The oldest correctly published post-Linnaean name for the species is *H. argutifolius* (1824) which refers to the spiny-toothed leaves and is therefore very descriptive of the plant but is perhaps slightly less pleasing to the ear. It is also not likely to be readily accepted by gardeners who have become accustomed to the more catchy epithet *corsicus* which denotes its place of origin.

The Corsican Hellebore has been known and cultivated since at least 1625 when it was illustrated as '*Helleborus niger trifoliatus*' by Aldini, from plants growing in the gardens of the Villa Farnese at Rome. Surprisingly Linnaeus (1753) did not provide it with a name but treated it as an unnamed variety of *H. foetidus*, a species which is instantly distinguishable on account of its pedate leaves with several narrow leaflets. Since Aldini's clearly recognisable illustration is cited in the original description of *H. argutifolius* by Viviani (1824), this drawing, and that of Morison (*Pl. Hist. Univ. Oxon.* 3: 460, t. 4, fig. 7 (1699)) which is also cited, may be taken as the types of the species since a type herbarium specimen does not appear to exist.

H. argutifolius is one of the species which, together with *H. foetidus* and *H. lividus*, produces a rather woody stem bearing leaves and a terminal inflorescence, basal leaves being entirely absent. It is a very distinctive robust plant with 3-lobed, spiky-margined leaves and a large cluster of cup-like pale green flowers, easily distinguished from its closest relative, the Majorcan *H. lividus*. The main points of distinction are as follows:

H. lividus: Plant rarely exceeding 45 cm in height; leaves with smooth margins or occasionally with a few well-spaced teeth, especially when young, dark green with very obvious whitish veins giving a marbled appearance; undersurface of leaf suffused with pinkish-brown; inflorescence lax with few (less than 10) flowers; flowers green, usually suffused pinkish-brown.

H. argutifolius: Plant up to 120 cm in height, sometimes more; leaflets coarsely spiny-toothed, mid-green with veins more or less the same colour, therefore not very conspicuous; undersurface of leaf green; inflorescence dense containing many (15–30) flowers; flowers pale green.

One might also comment that from the point of view of the horticulturist there is a marked difference in hardiness between the two, *H. argutifolius* being a very hardy plant in Britain whereas *H. lividus* is much less tough and readily succumbs to frost even in the south of England.

When brought together in gardens the two will hybridise to produce variable intermediates which tend to cloud these differences but if specimens of the true species are placed side by side there is to my mind absolutely no doubt as to their distinctness. Taxonomic opinion does however vary on this point and some botanists have merged *H. lividus* and *H. argutifolius*, treating them as subspecies. Under these circumstances the oldest epithet for the species as a whole is *H. lividus* (1789) and the Majorcan plant accordingly becomes subsp. *lividus*, while the prior epithet at subspecies level for the Corsican Hellebore is not *argutifolius* but *corsicus*, so it takes the name *H. lividus* subsp. *corsicus*. This apparently confusing situation is brought about because under the Rules of Nomenclature the priority rule only applies within each separate taxonomic rank (ie species, subspecies, etc.) so that an epithet such as *corsicus* has no priority outside its own rank. Applying these rules, at species level *argutifolius* is the oldest epithet but at the rank of subspecies, *corsicus* wins the day. For the reasons explained above, I consider these two Hellebores to be clearly distinct as species, hence *H. argutifolius* is the correct name for the Corsican plant.

Although confined to just two islands in the Mediterranean it appears that there is no threat to the continued existence of *H. argutifolius*, whereas the position of *H. lividus* on Majorca is less secure. It is fairly common throughout the entire island of Corsica over a wide range of altitude and habitat. On Sardinia it seems also to be widely scattered although it is possibly not so abundant. Various observations about it in the wild are worth repeating since they represent eye-witness accounts by knowledgeable plantsmen. A.Q. Wells, writing in the *Bulletin* of the Alpine Garden Society 20: 25 (1952) states that the inflorescences sometimes sprawl along the ground and that it occurs from sea level to over 2135 metres. Will Ingwersen, in *Bulletin* 2: 182 (1934) noted a wide range of habitats from arid hillsides to shady ravines and moist stream beds and said that it seemed equally content in any aspect or situation. He also remarked that he received a stinging irritation while extracting seeds and his fingers became seriously blistered. Jim Archibald in *Bulletin* 31: 208 (1963), commenting on the variability in stature of *H. argutifolius*, noted that it reached a gawky 6 ft (1.8 m) when growing up through maquis (scrub) but only a compact 3 ft (0.9 m) in open hill pastures.

Apart from these variations, which are probably largely due to environment, the species is remarkably uniform in appearance. Schiffner (1889) does however distinguish forms with narrow leaflets (f. *angustifolius*) and broad leaflets (f. *latifolius*).

Cultivation

Not surprisingly with a plant which is so tolerant of a wide range of habitats and altitudes in its native environment, *H. argutifolius* is an easy-going plant in cultivation and is successful in most garden situations, although extremes of dampness and drought are best avoided. The most vigorous and floriferous specimens are usually obtained in deep, fairly rich soil in full sun or partial shade, conditions which keep the plants reasonably compact and weather resistant. In heavy shade it becomes rather 'leggy' and is liable to fall over during inclement weather. Self-sown seedlings are likely to appear when the plants are growing well and in fact seeds present the only really practical method of propagation. These should be collected and sown when mature in early summer and will then normally germinate the following autumn, winter or spring. The time taken for the seedlings to reach flowering size largely depends upon the cultivation methods. There are reports of flowering in one year from seed sowing but it is much more likely to involve a period of two or three years. Seedlings are best planted in their permanent positions while they are still young with one or two proper leaves (as distinct from the two non-spiny cotyledons) and should preferably be left undisturbed to grow on to maturity, at which time they may be a metre or more across, so plenty of room should be allowed when planting out. There is little maintenance required but it is a worthwhile practice to prune out the old flowering stems down to the base, thus allowing the new young stems to develop vigorously. Obviously this is best done soon after flowering but if seeds are required it must be delayed until they have been gathered.

Being an evergreen species *H. argutifolius* can act as a winter host for the black spot diseases so it is a wise precaution to check over the plants during autumn and winter and prune off any infected leaflets, and spray with fungicide from time to time. Further comments about these diseases will be found under the appropriate section on page 159.

The Corsican Hellebore is an imposing species which may be planted with good effect in a variety of garden situations. Since it flowers early in the year it associates well with spring bulbs and its bold green foliage is of interest throughout the winter. It is very suitable for planting in front of and between winter-flowering deciduous shrubs such as *Viburnum farreri* and *Daphne mezereum* to enhance a winter border.

H. argutifolius Viviani, Fl. Cors. Prodr. 1: 8 (1824).

Type: Corsica, 'prope Figari'. No specimen of this collection has been traced but Viviani refers to the illustrations in Aldini, *Descr. Pl. Hort. Farnes.*: 93 (1625) and Morison, *Pl. Hist. Univ. Oxon.* 3: 460, Sect. 12, t. 4, fig. 7 (1699), both as 'H. niger trifoliatus'; these are acceptable in lieu of a type specimen.

Synonyms

H. corsicus Willd., Enum. Hort. Berol. Suppl. 40 (1813) nomen nudum; probably refers to this species but is unacceptable in the absence of a description.

H. lividus Aiton, Hort. Kew. ed. 1, 2: 272 (Aug.–Sept. 1789) not Aiton in Curtis Bot. Mag. 2: t. 72 (Jan. 1789)

H. triphyllus Lam. var., Encycl. Méth. 3: 97 (Oct. 1789)

H. spinescens Tausch ex Schiffner in Engl. Bot. Jahrb. 11: 103 (1889)

H. corsicus subsp. *corsicus* f. *latifolius* Schiffner, loc. cit.

H. corsicus subsp. *corsicus* f. *angustifolius* Schiffner, loc. cit.

H. trifolius Mill. var. *serratifolius* (DC.) Gürke in Richter, Pl. Eur. 2: 410 (1903)

H. trifolius subsp. *corsicus* Briquet, Prodr. Fl. Corse 1: 582 (1910)

H. lividus subsp. *corsicus* (Briquet) Tutin in Feddes Repert. 69: 53 (1964); invalid since it is based on *H. corsicus* Willd.

H. lividus subsp. *corsicus* (Briquet) Yeo in Taxon 35: 157 (1986)

Description

Glabrous perennial herb up to 1.2 m (sometimes to 1.8 m) in height with a tough rhizomatous rootstock giving rise to erect or sprawling leafy stems of annual duration, dying after fruiting to be replaced by new ones. Basal leaves absent. Leaves all borne on the stem, trifoliate, leathery, long-petiolate; petioles pale green; leaflets 8–23 cm long, 3.5–6.5 cm wide, acute at the apex, dissimilar in shape, the central one regularly elliptical and wedge-shaped at the base, the lateral ones irregular, unequal-sided with the outer side rounded at the base; upper surface rather dull mid-green, the veins not markedly paler and thus not very conspicuous (cf. *H. lividus*); lower surface pale green; margins coarsely spinose-dentate. Inflorescence terminal, many-flowered, usually with about 15–30 flowers; lower bracts at base of inflorescence entire or with leaf-like outgrowths at the apex, upper bracts subtending the flowers entire, ovate or elliptic; pedicels usually about 2–6 cm long, pale green. Flowers pale green, cup-shaped or bowl-shaped, 2.5–5 cm diameter; perianth segments more or less equal, broadly ovate to elliptic or suborbicular, 1.2–2.6 cm long, 0.8–2.1 cm wide; nectaries about 10–14, shortly stalked, tubular with an oblique mouth, green; stamens numerous, erect but curving outwards and reflexing with age, anthers about 1–2 mm long; carpels 3–5, sessile, fused at the base; styles exceeding the stamens. Follicles c. 2–2.5 cm long (excluding the persistent style); seeds 3–4 mm long, dark brown with a fleshy whitish ridge (elaiosome) on one side.

Flowering time January to May in the wild, January–March in cultivation.

Habitat Rocky scrub (garigue and maquis), open hillsides, shady ravines, stream banks and grassy places, sea level to 2315 metres.

Distribution Corsica and Sardinia, widespread on both islands.

4 *Helleborus lividus*

H. lividus is a member of the caulescent group of species, lacking basal leaves and instead having tough stems which bear the leaves and terminal inflorescences. The stems die away after fruiting to be replaced by new ones which will produce flowers in the following season.

This delightful Majorcan endemic is a very distinctive plant not easily confused with any other Hellebore although it is related to, and hybridizes with, the Corsican *H. argutifolius* (*H. corsicus*). Hybrids are intermediate in their features and some variants of *H.* × *sternii*, as the hybrid is called, may be rather similar in appearance to the true *H. lividus* but even so it is usually easy enough to detect the presence of *H. argutifolius* characters. The most striking feature of *H. lividus* is the foliage which is a deep glossy or greyish green on the upper surface with a conspicuous netted pattern of cream or silver-coloured veins; the underside is usually suffused with a purplish stain, as are the petioles and main stems of the plant. The leaves consist of 3 leaflets, as in *H. argutifolius*, but are distinctive in that when mature they are either completely smooth on the margins or have a few widely-spaced shallow teeth, quite unlike the very coarsely and sharply toothed leaves of *H. argutifolius*; the young leaves of *H. lividus* may however be somewhat toothed. In overall stature *H. lividus* is smaller than its Corsican relative, usually less than 45 cm, but sometimes up to 60 cm in the wild, and the number of flowers in the inflorescence seldom exceeds ten, unlike the Corsican Hellebore which can have between fifteen and thirty flowers and reach nearly 2 metres in height in the wild.

The individual flowers of *H. lividus* are bowl-shaped at first, becoming shallower with age, and they are normally suffused with a pinkish-purple colour; those of *H. argutifolius* are a plain light green with no hint of purplish coloration. Occasionally forms of *H. lividus* occur in the wild which lack any purplish staining on flowers or leaves (such variants have been recorded by Mr & Mrs H. Crook) but the other characters given above still apply and there is no question of these particular specimens being intermediates with *H. argutifolius*.

There is a certain amount of doubt concerning the fragrance or otherwise of *H. lividus*. Barcelo in his *Flora de las Islas Baleares* (1879), comments on 'un olor nauseabundo', although he may be referring to *H. foetidus*; others have noted a pleasant fragrance or no smell at all.

The distinguishing features between this Majorcan plant and its Corsican relative are sufficient to regard them as distinct species and I cannot support the view that they should be merged into one species. If it is considered that two such different plants as this are best united then there is almost no argument for recognising the majority of the species in the acaulescent group (*H. viridis, H. dumetorum, H. odorus* etc.) which are far less distinct.

On the matter of nomenclature, the oldest post-Linnaean name for the Majorcan species is Philip Miller's *H. trifolius* (1768) but this epithet had already been used in *Helleborus* by Linnaeus himself in 1753 for the plant we now know as *Coptis trifolia*; thus *H. trifolius* Miller is unacceptable under the International Rules of Nomenclature. In chronological order the next name to appear was *H. lividus* Aiton, published in the second volume of Curtis' *Botanical Magazine*. This just preceded *H. triphyllus* of Lamarck by several months in early 1789. Aiton's name, clearly represented by plate 72 of the *Botanical Magazine*, thus becomes the valid epithet for this Majorcan species. Curiously, Aiton's use of the same epithet in *Hortus Kewensis*, dated several months later in late 1789, appears to refer to *H. argutifolius* (*H. corsicus*).

In the wild *H. lividus* is not a common plant and in conservation terms is given the status of 'rare' which means that although it is a scarce plant its existence is not considered to be under any threat at present. Some of its sites on Majorca are rather difficult of access and it seems likely that in these particular places there is little danger of development wiping out the habitat. As an example of the difficult terrain where it sometimes occurs, it is worth quoting from the article by A.Q. Wells in the *Bulletin* of the Alpine Garden Society Vol. 20: 25 (1952): '... the north side of the cliff several hundred feet high, gently dripping with water and covered in places with a calcareous deposit. ... about 800 ft above sea level down the slope to about 600 ft above the sea.' This does not mean that it only occurs in such places and in some sites it is quite readily accessible ('in carpet slippers' as Mr Phil Ballard once told me!). It is certainly not always as romantically situated as the A.G.S. *Bulletin* Vol. 2 (1933) would have us believe. To quote, 'It is found in one locality (an almost inaccessible cove frequented by smugglers and charcoal burners) in the island of Majorca.'!

Cultivation

H. lividus has been in cultivation for a long time, certainly over 200 years, for in 1789 William Aiton wrote (*Bot. Mag.* t. 72) that it was 'extraordinary that this plant which has for many years been cultivated in this country, should have escaped the notice of Linnaeus'. It is equally surprising that its country of origin was unknown to Aiton, for he noted that he and his colleagues were 'strangers to its place of growth'. According to Aiton it was in cultivation in England in 1710, although one must be careful here because in some instances he appears to be referring to the Corsican Hellebore as *H. lividus*.

It is unfortunate that this delightful plant is one of the least frost-resistant of all the species and is likely to be killed outright by prolonged cold periods. It is best, therefore, to choose a sheltered site away from cold winds but also partially shaded to avoid hot, dry conditions in summer. If it is grown outside it is as well to retain a few plants in the protection of a frame or greenhouse to avoid losing it altogether since the true plant is not easily replaced, being rarely offered in the nursery trade. *H. lividus* makes an attractive plant for pot cultivation in a cool glasshouse or frame, kept just frost-free in winter and then plunged outside in a semi-shaded spot for the summer. It is tolerant of both acid and alkaline soils but appears to prefer the latter; the best results are achieved using a light gritty soil mixture.

Seeds are produced quite readily but if *H. argutifolius* is cultivated nearby, and if no steps are taken to prevent cross-pollination, hybrids will almost certainly appear.

H. lividus Aiton in Curtis, *Bot. Mag.* t. 72 (1st Jan 1789).

Type: there appears to be no original herbarium specimen in existence but t. 72 of the *Bot. Mag.* may be taken as the type.

Synonyms

H. trifolius Miller, Gard. Dict. ed. 8, no. 4 (1768) nom. illegit., non Linn. (1753), which is *Coptis trifolia*.

H. triphyllus Lamarck var., Encycl. Méth. 3: 97 (1789)

H. lividus var. *integrifolius* DC. in Lam. Fl. Franç. 4: 907 (1805)

H. lividus var. *integrilobus* DC., Prodr. 1; 47 (1824)

H. corsicus subsp. *lividus* (Aiton) Schiffner in Engl. Bot. Jahrb. 11: 103 (1889)

H. corsicus subsp. *lividus* var. *pictus* Schiffner, loc. cit.: 104

H. corsicus subsp. *lividus* forma *angustifolius* Schiffner, loc. cit.: 103

H. corsicus subsp. *lividus* forma *latifolius* Schiffner, loc. cit.

H. triphyllos var. *integrifolius* (DC.) Gürke in Pl. Europ. 11: 410 (1903)

H. trifolius subsp. *lividus* (Aiton) Briquet in Prodr. Fl. Cors. 1: 582 (1910)

H. trifolius var. *lividus* (Aiton) Knoche, Fl. Balear. 1: 477 (1921)

H. argutifolius, the Corsican Hellebore

H. atrorubens, the true wild form from
N. Yugoslavia

H. dumetorum, near Radkersburg in S.
Austria

H. viridis subsp. *viridis* in cultivation

Description

Glabrous perennial herb up to 45 cm (rarely 60 cm) high with a tough rhizomatous rootstock giving rise to erect or sprawling leafy stems of annual duration but present in winter, dying after fruiting to be replaced by new ones. Basal leaves absent. Leaves all borne on the stem, trifoliolate, leathery, long-petiolate; petioles suffused purple; leaflets 10–20 cm long, 5–10 cm wide, acute at the apex, dissimilar in shape, the central one regularly elliptical and wedge-shaped at the base, the lateral ones unequal-sided, with the outer side rounded at the base; upper surface deep green with conspicuous pale creamy or silvery reticulated veins; lower surface usually suffused pinkish-purple; margins usually untoothed on mature leaves or with well-spaced shallow serrations, the young leaves often somewhat more toothed. Inflorescence terminal, usually with less than 10 flowers; lower bracts at base of inflorescence 3-lobed, like small leaves, upper bracts subtending the flowers entire, ovate or elliptic; pedicels usually 2–6 cm long, purplish-suffused. Flowers creamy green suffused pinkish-purple, bowl-shaped to flattish, usually 3–5 cm in diameter (rarely to 7.5 cm); sepals more or less equal, broadly elliptic, ovate or suborbicular, 2.5–4 cm long, 1.7–3.2 cm wide; nectaries about 10, shortly stalked, tubular with an oblique mouth, green or pinkish-purple; stamens numerous, erect, curving outwards and reflexing with age, anthers about 1–2 mm long; carpels usually 5, rarely 3, 4 or 6, sessile, fused at the base; styles just exceeding the stamens. Follicles c. 1.5–2 cm long (excluding the persistent style); seeds c. 3 mm long, dark brown with a fleshy whitish ridge (elaiosome) on one side.

Flowering time December–March in the wild and in cultivation.

Habitat Woods and open hill slopes, rocky valleys, 40–1400 metres altitude.

Distribution Majorca, where it is uncommon but in widespread localities. It is recorded at various places throughout the mountain ranges along the northwest coast, for example at Soller, Monte Galatzó, Andraitx to Estalenchs, Sierra de Torrellas, Puig Mayor, Valldemosa, Sierra de Alfabia, Puig Roig, Ternellas and Planici. From the east of the island it is noted as occurring near Artá and Font d'es Barraca, and it is also recorded on Cabrera Is. south of Majorca. Whether it exists today in all these localities is doubtful.

SECTION FOUR

Helleborus

5 *Helleborus niger*

There is little need to introduce the Christmas Rose for it is likely to be the Hellebore which most people first encounter, whether gardeners or not, since it is such a popular subject for Christmas cards and calendars. Unfortunately, in practice, it is rarely in flower for the festive season and as a wild plant it is certainly spring-flowering. In its homelands in the central and eastern Alps of Europe its buds normally appear at the first hint of spring after the snow melts and it is only when brought into our lowland gardens that it flowers somewhat earlier, usually in late winter. However, with the protection of a cloche, it can be encouraged into early growth and may provide some of the much sought-after snowy white blooms for December 25th. When grown from seed there is a lot of morphological variation in *H. niger* and there is certainly also variation in flowering time among seedlings, so some selection for earliness is worthwhile. A visit to a nurseryman who is growing Hellebores from seed is always interesting, to pick out different forms. In times past it was regularly cultivated for the Christmas trade although a certain amount of forcing was practised and in the last century it was recommended that plants should be lifted and potted for flowering in the conservatory. At times *H. niger* has been grown also for the cut flower market, on Christmas Rose farms according to Canon Ellacombe, which implies that that they were being extensively cultivated rather than imported directly from the wild; however there was also a large trade in wild plants in the 19th century, thousands being collected in Austria for importation into England.

Although *H. niger* was one of the earliest known of the Hellebores and appears frequently in herbals and old horticultural literature it is not the easiest of the species to grow, and one seldom sees good plants of it in gardens. Even when it is doing well it never grows and seeds with such abandon as the Lenten Rose, *H. orientalis*.

Of the acaulescent Hellebores, *H. niger* is one of the most distinctive with its leathery deep green pedate leaves which are scarcely toothed on the margins, but may have coarse teeth at the apex of the leaflets. The large flattish glistening white flowers, usually one per stem, are easily distinguishable from those of all other species, even from the white forms of *H. orientalis* which are usually nearer to cream in colour. Given only an individual flower, the identity can immediately be confirmed by checking the bracts on the pedicel, for in *H. niger* these are undivided and without teeth whereas in *H. orientalis*, and most other acaulescent species, they are divided in a leaf-like manner and have conspicuous teeth.

Apart from being morphologically very distinct it has been shown by Joan Nowicke and John Skvarla (1983) that in its pollen characters *H. niger* 'is the sole species in the genus with a continuous tectum'. The distinctness has resulted in the inevitable isolation of *H. niger* in systems of classification and in the opinion of Spach (1839) it was the only representative of his Section Chionorhodon (literally 'Snow Rose'). This view was followed by the two major monographers Schiffner (1889) and Ulbrich (1938). Nowicke & Skvarla expressed the view that 'pollen morphology reinforces the distinction and thus the separate sectional status'. Clearly, then, the realistic approach is to recognise a Section for *H. niger* on its own so I have likewise followed Spach in this, but his name for the Section cannot be retained for the following reason. Linnaeus in 1753 did not indicate which was the type species of his genus *Helleborus* and this was not resolved until 1913 when N.L. Britton & A. Brown chose *H. niger* as the type (called a lectotype); this was later confirmed by A.S. Hitchcock & M.L. Green in the *International Rules of Botanical Nomenclature* (1935), and there is no reason to object to this view. This choice of *H. niger* as the type of the genus means that the Section to which it belongs automatically takes on the generic name as well, so that *H. niger* must belong to Section Helleborus (Syn. Section Chionorhodon Spach).

H. niger is a very variable species, both in the wild and in cultivated stock, and many of the variants have been named, albeit rather haphazardly, over the years and often without good descriptions so that it is impossible to say exactly what some of the cultivars were like. Although taxonomically speaking most of the variation is of little significance, it may be important horticulturally and it is worth reviewing those variants which have been given distinguishing names. I suspect that in some cases, however, names such as 'Cheshire Form', 'Scottish Form' etc., mentioned in the 19th century, were just well grown plants from districts where the species happened to thrive and that in less favourable conditions the apparent distinctiveness would be lost.

Considering first of all *H. niger* in its wild state it does seem that, broadly speaking, two variants can be recognised, and these, having some geographical significance, can be regarded as subspecies. Schiffner (1890) originated this concept, although Freyn had already described *macranthus* as a variety in 1881, and this subspecific classification was followed more recently by Merxmüller and Podlech (1961) and *Flora Europaea* (1964). The two may be distinguished as follows:

subsp. *niger*
Leaf segments oblong-cuneate, dark green, serrate towards the apex. Flowers up to 8 cm in diameter. This has a wide distribution from Switzerland and Germany to Austria, Italy and Yugoslavia.

subsp. *macranthus* (Freyn) Schiffner
Leaf segments broadly lanceolate, bluish-green or grey-green, spinulose-serrate. Flowers 8–11 cm in diameter. Distributed only in Italy and northern Jugoslavia.

It should be noted that in *Flora Europaea*, and in several other works, the perianth segments of subsp. *niger* are said to be 'often pinkish, broadly ovate' whereas those of subsp. *macranthus* are 'usually white, ovate', indicating that those of the latter are narrower and do not generally have the pinkish suffusion. Freyn, however, in the original description of his var. *macranthus*, states that the segments are suborbicular and pale pink on the exterior. Such discrepancies indicate that a really thorough field study of *H. niger* is required, throughout its range, to assess the validity of the stated differences.

In addition to these two subspecies there have been numerous varieties and cultivars of *H. niger* described and although many of them are not now to be found in cultivation it is worth listing these for interest's sake and as an indication of the range of variation in the species. Some of these may be directly referable to one or the other of the above subspecies but in the garden environment it is reasonable to assume that hybridisation will have occurred and at least some of these are likely to be intermediates, obscuring the already somewhat cloudy distinguishing characteristics of the two subspecies!

Much has been written about the relative height of leaves and flowers in subsp. *macranthus* as if this were one of the important features but it seems to me that this is not the case. Freyn made no mention of this character and gave the flower size (hence the name) and colour, and the colour of the foliage, as the distinguishing characteristics. The feature of leaves overtopping the flowers seems to be the normal condition for *H. niger* in the wild, although often the foliage tends to spread out and lie almost flat allowing the flowers to stand up. In cultivation forms have certainly been selected in which the flowers are carried on long stalks above the leaves, and vice versa, but this appears to be a variable feature throughout the species and cannot be utilised as an additional point of distinction between subsp. *niger* and subsp. *macranthus*.

The problem in maintaining any selected variant of *H. niger* in cultivation is that it requires vegetative propagation if its offspring are to be identical, and this is a slow and laborious business. From seed there is likely to be variation, as noted by the famous 19th century grower of Hellebores, William Brockbank of Brockhurst, Didsbury. He grew hundreds of plants of *H. niger* and noted what extreme variation there was, although at the same time his writings show that he was reluctant just to lump them under one species and he mentions a number of these variations as if they were distinct entities. The 1889 catalogue of Barr & Sons listed 9 selections of Christmas Rose, one of which was said to be fragrant whilst another had variegated foliage.

Undoubtedly the slow vegetative propagation as opposed to rapid but variable sexual propagation by seed is the main reason why the older cultivars are no longer available. Most selections make but a fairly fleeting appearance in the horticultural world and few of the following named variants will be found today. I have listed those described as varieties first, in alphabetical order, followed by the cultivars.

var. *altifolius* Hayne (*H. altifolius* (Hayne) Reichb.) In this variant the leaves overtop the flowers, the stems and petioles are purple-spotted, the leaflets coarsely serrate and the large flowers have tepals which are rather long and narrow, scarcely overlapping. It is almost certainly a form of subsp. *macranthus*. There is a beautiful illustration in Hayne's *Getreue Darstellung und Beschreibung Arzneykunde Gebräuchlichen Gewächse*, Vol. 1, t. 8 (Berlin 1805). William Brockbank describes a specimen of var. *altifolius* which he grew as having robust flower stalks each carrying two flowers, one of which was over 5 inches (12 cm) across!

In literature var. *altifolius* is often given as being synonymous with subsp. *macranthus* and is frequently mentioned as flowering early, in November or December.

var. angustifolius Sweet. This was described as a narrow leaved form, in contrast to var. *latifolius* which is apparently the same as, or a variant of, subsp. *macranthus*. It was rather small-flowered. Much was written in the 19th and early 20th centuries, especially in the *Gardeners' Chronicle*, about this and other forms of *H. niger* and clearly there was a great deal of confusion over the different forms; even within a variety such as *angustifolius* two variants were recognised, one from Scotland with pink-suffused flowers known as '*H. niger scoticus*' and one from the Manchester area with pure white flowers. The former was probably the same as the 'Wardie Lodge' selection mentioned below.

var. humilifolius Hayne. This was described at the same time as var. *altifolius* and represents the reverse condition where the flowers overtop the leaves; the stems are unspotted, less coarsely toothed and the flowers have relatively broader tepals. It presumably represents a form of subsp. *niger*.

var. laciniatus Gusmus ex Hegi. Here, the leaves are said to be finely divided but I think it more likely that the epithet refers to narrow leaflets rather than more of them; it would thus be comparable with var. *angustifolius*.

var. oblongifolius Beck. A form in which the leaves have a rather elongated central leaflet, narrowing abruptly at its base.

var. stenopetalus Beck. Here, the tepals are said to be about three times as long as they are wide.

CULTIVARS of *H. niger*

'Brockhurst' This, according to William Brockbank who lived at Brockhurst, was grown alongside 'St. Brigid' (see below) for comparison and found to be the same. 19th century.

'De Graff's Var.' This might be an interesting form as the flowers were said to change to pale primrose as they matured.

'Grandiflorus' (*H. grandiflorus* Salisb.) is a synonym of subsp. *macranthus*.

'Ladham's Var.' A large-flowered form which was considered by Sir Frederick Stern to be the same as 'Potter's Wheel'.

'Louis Cobbett' A large form probably dating from the 1950s in which the flowers have a strong pink suffusion; it is often referred to as 'Lewis Cobbett.'

'Major' This appears to be a synonym of subsp. *macranthus*, a large-flowered form, offered in the Barr catalogues of the 1880s.

'Maximus' A synonym of subsp. *macranthus*. Very large rose-tinted flowers; late 19th century.

'Minor' A name attached to small forms imported from Austria in the 19th century.

'Madame Fourcade' This was said to be of dwarf habit with light green foliage and large pure white flowers. 19th century.

'Potter's Wheel' A more recent cultivar than most, which can still be found in catalogues from time to time. It has large well-formed rounded flowers with a distinct green eye. It is sometimes offered as a 'strain', the plants grown from seed and varying somewhat. According to Mr Michael G. Tristram, this arose as a seedling in the garden of his grandfather, Major G.H. Tristram, and was introduced to the trade by Hilda Davenport-Jones.

'Praecox' An early-flowering form, usually evident before Christmas. It had large rounded flowers in pure white with a conspicuous green eye and was said to breed reasonably true from seed.

'Riverston' A form raised by J.T. Poë and mentioned by E.B. Anderson as being known from the time of his youth. Said to be an early-flowering form with long stalks, and fragrant.

'St. Brigid' This is sometimes mentioned in literature as '*H. juvernis*'. It is a famous Irish cultivar from the last century, named by Frederick Burbidge, Curator of Trinity College Botanic Garden, Dublin, after an authoress called Mrs Lawrenson who used Saint Brigid as a pseudonym. It was discovered, according to Dr Charles Nelson in his delightful garden plant history book *An Irish Flower Garden*, in a garden in Kildare in about 1850. The main feature of this cultivar was that the deep rich green foliage overtopped and hid the flowers, thus protecting them from inclement winter weather.

'The Bath Variety' A selection which was cultivated in the area of Bath in the 19th century for the winter flower market. It was of robust growth with striking bold green foliage and large flowers.

'Trotter's Form' This was offered by Jack Drake of Inshriach in the early 1980s. It has large flowers, white turning to apricot with age, and it continues to flower at intervals through the year. It was raised by Dick Trotter, renowned for his work with Asiatic gentians.

'Wardie Lodge' This was grown in Scotland by Miss F.J. Hope of Wardie Lodge during the late 19th century. It was a narrow-leaved variant with purple-mottled leaf and flower stalks and had large white flowers tinged pink on the outside. It was probably the same as that grown as var. *angustifolius*.

'Vernalis' (*H. vernalis* hort.) A very vigorous form with glaucous green foliage and white flowers tinged purple, which were said to be fragrant.

In addition to these variants there was once a double-flowered form collected by a Mr Koeppen in the late 19th century at Scheibbs in Austria; the stamens were white and petaloid.

Cultivation

Although one of the best-known species, *H. niger* is one of the least easy to grow successfully. It will not settle down and seed itself around with great abandon in the way that *H. orientalis* and its forms do. The best plants I ever grew were at the edge of a vegetable garden in dappled shade. The soil was a very stony (sandstone) loam, deeply cultivated to at least 45 cm with a lot of humus added, mostly in the form of rotted beech leaves; the pH was just on the acid side of neutral, just sufficient to grow Rhododendrons if peat was added. I mention this because it is often said that *H. niger* is best on alkaline soils. I think this is generally true but it will also tolerate slightly acid conditions if other factors are satisfactory. It will certainly take to heavy soils if plenty of well-rotted humus is added, but this should not be in the form of very fresh manure. I also fed my plants with a proprietary liquid manure in the spring and summer, at about fortnightly intervals. In autumn or winter, before the buds began to expand I sprinkled coarse sand in and around the crowns to prevent splashing of the blooms during rain storms and I think this was well worthwhile, but bark chips might be a better and more attractive substitute.

H. niger does not thrive if it is moved frequently so it is best to obtain young plants and leave them undisturbed. Obviously if plenty are available then the practice of lifting and potting them for a winter dispay is possible, but after forcing and disturbance they will take a good while to settle down again. Alternatively a cloche can be placed over plants *in situ* and this will have some advancing effect on the flowering time, and protect them from inclement weather.

Propagation by seed it not quite so rapid as it is with *H. orientalis* but seeds are produced fairly readily and they will normally germinate the following winter if sown fresh. Apart from some natural variation in the seedlings, they come 'true' since there is little chance of hybridisation taking place with other species. *H. niger* will however occasionally cross with the very distinct caulescent species *H. argutifolius* and *H. lividus* (and their hybrid *H. × sternii*) which is somewhat surprising. The *H. niger × H. argutifolius* hybrids are quite attractive and combine the different growth habits of the two species in a curious way. These hybrids, known collectively as *H. × nigercors* Stooke ex Wall, produce basal leaves and an aerial leafy stem with flowers arising both from ground level and from the apex of the stem as in *H. argutifolius*. The flowers are larger than those of the latter and are whiter and more widely saucer-shaped, but not as pure white nor as flat as they are in *H. niger*. There are further comments about these hybrids on page 142.

Propagation by division of the rhizomes is the only feasible method of increase if it is wished to perpetuate a particular form. This is best done with a sharp knife in autumn and the divisions, each with a growing point, are potted up and kept in a frame or glasshouse. A little heat seems to be beneficial in getting them started.

H. niger Linn., Species Plantarum: 558 (1753).
Type: 'Habitat in Austria, Hetruria, Apenninis'.

(a) subsp. *niger*

Synonyms
H. niger var. *typicus* Beck, Fl. Nieder-Österreich; 396 (1890)

Description
Glabrous perennial herb up to 30 cm but usually about 15–20 cm in height, with a tough rhizomatous rootstock. Leaves basal, overwintering, pedate with 7–9 segments, leathery, deep green, the segments oblong or oblanceolate, 5–20 cm long, 2.5–7 cm wide, cuneate at the base, acute or obtuse and toothed towards the apex; petioles 10–25 cm long, green or purple-spotted. Inflorescences usually (in wild material) shorter than the leaves, sometimes equalling them, often 1-flowered but sometimes there are 2 or 3 flowers; peduncles stout, 5–20 cm long, green or purple-spotted, bearing 1 or 2 bracts just below the flower; bracts ovate or obovate, entire, pale green, 1–3 cm long. Flowers white, usually greenish in the centre and often changing to pinkish or purplish with age, flattish, 4.5–8 cm in diameter; perianth segments usually subequal, broadly ovate, broadly elliptic or suborbicular, rounded or obtuse at apex, 2–4 cm long, 1.5–4 cm wide; nectaries 12–20, stalked, curved-tubular with an oblique or somewhat notched mouth, green; stamens numerous, erect or suberect, not reflexing with age, anthers about 1–2 mm long; carpels 5–8, fused at the base, usually some of them not developing to maturity; styles exceeding the stamens, curved outwards. Follicles 2–2.5 cm long (excluding the persistent style); seeds 4–5 mm long, brown with large whitish elaiosome (oil body).

Flowering time (February–)March–June in the wild. (November–)December–March in cultivation.

Habitat Mountain woods, copses or valleys on limestone formations, sometimes in grassy alpine pastures, 400–2000 metres.

Distribution Austria, S. Germany, C. and N. Italy, Switzerland, N. Yugoslavia. Doubtfully native in France; Coste in *Flore de la France* (1901) indicates 'Basses Alpes & Hautes Alpes' but Fournier in *Les Quatre Flores de la France*, ed. 2 (1977) only includes it with a question mark.

H. viridis subsp. *occidentalis* at Four Elms in Kent

H. viridis subsp. *occidentalis* at Four Elms in Kent

H. odorus in cultivation

H. multifidus subsp. *hercegovinus* near Dubrovnik, Yugoslavia

H. multifidus subsp. *hercegovinus*
mature foliage

H. multifidus subsp. *istriacus* near
Rijeka, N.W. Yugoslavia

H. multifidus subsp. *bocconei* on Mt
Pollino, Italy. (Photo: H & M Crook)

H. thibetanus, herbarium specimen
from Szechuan, China

H. x *sternii* in Molly Crook's garden at
Harpenden, Herts

H. x *sternii* 'Boughton Beauty'

H. lividus x *H. niger*

H. x *nigercors* 'Alabaster'

(b) subsp. *macranthus* (Freyn) Schiffner in Bot. Jahrb. 11: 105 (1889).

Type: Italy, Lombardia, Val Malenga, *F. Maly*, cultivated in Vienna (?specimen in Vienna).

Synonyms
H. niger var. *macranthus* Freyn in Flora 64; 14: 209 (1881)
H. macranthus (Freyn) Dalla Torre & Sarnth., Fl. Tirol 6, 2: 228 (1909)

Description
Similar to subsp. *niger* but leaf segments broadly lanceolate, bluish-green or slightly glaucous, spinulose–serrate; flowers 8–11 cm in diameter; perianth segments 4–6 cm long.

Flowering time as for subsp. *niger.*

Habitat as for subsp. *niger.*

Distribution N. Italy, N. Yugoslavia.

SECTION FIVE

Helleborastrum

6 *Helleborus orientalis*

Although the Christmas Rose, *H. niger*, has the distinction of being the most widely publicised Hellebore, when it comes to the question of garden value there is no doubt that *H. orientalis*, with all its many variations, is by far the superior plant, easily cultivated, increasing freely by seed and much more floriferous than its rather more aristocratic but fussy relative. This ability to vary, and to hybridise with other species, opens the way to horticultural success for this species, since it allows for the selection of an almost endless range of possibilities.

The garden-raised forms are discussed in Chapter 7, so here we will confine ourselves to the wild *H. orientalis*, its history and post-Linnaean nomenclature, which in itself creates problems. We are, fortunately, assisted in this by the fact that *H. orientalis* is the only species occurring in the Black Sea region, although, as we shall see later, some authors have made attempts to divide it into several. The *Helleborus* from this region was apparently unknown to Linnaeus who, in *Species Plantarum* (1753), described only *H. niger*, *H. viridis* and *H. foetidus*, along with two others which have subsequently been removed from the genus, *H. trifolia* (= *Coptis trifolia*) and *H. hyemalis* (= *Eranthis hyemalis*). It was however known in the early 18th century to J.P. de Tournefort who believed that this was the true Black Hellebore, as used by the ancient physicians. Tournefort's specimen from his travels in the Levant in 1700 is held in the Paris herbarium and appears to represent the plant which we now call *H. orientalis*. Further supportive evidence for this is provided by the label which states in Tournefort's own handwriting. '*Helleborus niger Ponticus*', indicating a Turkish provenance; he has also added '*legitimus antiquorum*' showing that he regarded this as the genuine Hellebore of the ancients (see also p. 10). A further label has been attached with the following description: '*Helleborus niger, orientalis, amplissimo folio, caule prealto, flore purpurascente*'. The specimen and its labels, coupled with Tournefort's comments in one of his absorbing letters published in *Relation d'un voyage du Levant* (1717) clearly show that his remarks were directed towards the Turkish material, for he says that it was very common at the foot of Mount Olympus (Ulu Dağ), although he does also say that it was the same species as that found in Anticyra, Greece. This indicates that he included in his *H. niger orientalis* the Greek plant which we now refer to as *H. cyclophyllus*.

All of this, however fascinating, does not provide us with the correct post-Linnaean name and for this we must advance to 1789 and J.B. Lamarck who was aware of Tournefort's work, although he too included under *H. orientalis* the Greek material (i.e. *H. cyclophyllus*). He called it the 'Hellébore du Levant' and remarked that 'cette plante est commune dans les Isles d'Anticyre qui sont vis-à-vis le Mont Oeta, dans le Golfe de Zeiton, près de Nègrepont; elle l'est encore plus sur les bords du Pont-Euxin (la mer Noire), and sur-tout au pied du Mont Olympe [Ulu Dağ] en Asie, proche la Ville de Pruse [= Bursa]'. I think in view of the fact that Lamarck's epithet *orientalis* is clearly based upon the previous observations of Tournefort, who was referring primarily to Turkish specimens, it is justifiable to regard *H. orientalis* Lamarck as the correct and valid name for the Hellebore which occurs in north western and northern Turkey and the Caucasus, and with which we are so familiar in gardens as the Lenten Rose. The species was beautifully illustrated in 1827 as *H. officinalis* in Sibthorp and Smith's sumptuous *Flora Graeca* 6: tab. 523 but it was clearly indicated that this was the same as Lamarck's *H. orientalis*, so the name has no standing other than as a synonym.

The history of *H. orientalis* and its variants moves on to the 1840s when the Horticultural Society (later the R.H.S.) received two plants from H.M. Consul at Brusa (Bursa), a Mr Sandison, which had been collected on the Bithynian Olympus (Ulu Dağ), the same area as that mentioned first by Tournefort and then by Lamarck. John Lindley, at that time the Professor of Botany at University College and the vice-secretary of the Horticultural Society, decided that these were sufficiently distinct to merit recognition as separate species, one of which he referred to as *H. orientalis*, noting that 'at last this rare and interesting species, the genuine '*Elleborus melas*' (= black) of the ancients, has been obtained for our gardens'. The other plant he described as a new species, *H. olympicus*, in the Botanical Register 14, miscellaneous notes 54 (1841). Points of distinction from *H. orientalis* included smaller palmate (rather than pedate) leaves with narrower leaflets, and smaller green flowers. The following year in the *Botanical Register* for 1842 both plants were nicely illustrated in tab. 34 (*H. orientalis*) and tab. 58 (*H. olympicus*), showing that Lindley had indeed received two rather different forms and, quite understandably, had decided that they could not belong to the same species, since he had none of the intermediate forms of which we now have a better knowledge. The plant illustrated as *H. orientalis* had rather large flowers with broad somewhat wavy segments in white tinged with purple while the other, *H. olympicus*, had smaller creamy flowers tinged green and the segments were scarcely undulate at all. In my experience, however, the range of variation in wild populations of *H. orientalis* easily embraces these two forms.

The next major step in the taxonomy and nomenclature of *H. orientalis* and its allies involved the Berlin Botanic Garden in the 1850s. Many Hellebores were being introduced to the Garden, no doubt forming the basis for the exciting range of hybrids which were produced in Europe in the late 19th century. Alexander Braun, the Director of the Berlin Botanic Garden, in an appendix to the 1853 seed list, described *H. antiquorum*, *H. caucasicus*, *H. ponticus*, *H. abchasicus* and *H. guttatus*. Since these are all part of the *H. orientalis* complex it is worth reviewing each of them in turn, if only to dispose of the names.

H. antiquorum represented yet another collection 'ex Olympo Bithynico' (Ulu Dağ), and was, in effect, a new name for the plant depicted as *H. orientalis* in the *Botanical Register* of 1842, tab. 34, since A. Braun cited this illustration. By giving it the name *antiquorum*, 'of the ancients', it is clear that Braun was referring to the same species as that described by Tournefort and Lamarck, which they believed to be the true Black Hellebore of Dioscorides. *H. antiquorum* should thus be reduced to synonymy under *H. orientalis*.

H. caucasicus was described by Braun as differing from the other *H. orientalis* variants in having one basal leaf instead of two, and a rather short inflorescence held at an oblique angle; however these features seem to vary considerably and are probably of little significance. The flowers were said to be '*lutescentes*' (becoming greenish-yellow) or greenish with a purple suffusion, presumably starting a somewhat paler colour, again a not unusual state of affairs in *H. orientalis*, although it does seem to me that the Caucasian representatives tend to have slightly greener flowers than those occurring farther to the west in Turkey where creamy or whitish forms predominate. Again, the differences are insufficient to distinguish *H. caucasicus* from *H. orientalis*. The *Flora of the U.S.S.R.* maintains the name *H. caucasicus* for these cream and greenish Hellebores of the Caucasus and does not acknowledge the existence of *H. orientalis* in the Soviet Union. *H. ponticus* A. Braun seems to have been based on yet another slight variant of *H. orientalis*, this one originating from the Trabzon area of Turkey where the species abounds. Thus *H. caucasicus* and *H. ponticus* can join the list of synonyms of *H. orientalis*.

The next two, *H. abchasicus* and *H. guttatus*, are rather more interesting variants and are probably worth maintaining as subspecies since their flower colours make them at least horticulturally distinct and they do occur in a discrete area within the total range of *H. orientalis*.

H. abchasicus was a name used in gardens for a purple-flowered Caucasian Hellebore some time before A. Braun received a plant in Berlin and formally described it as a new species in 1853. Karl Koch, who was a colleague of Braun's and also at one time a Director of the Berlin Botanic Garden, traced its early history and the way in which it was disseminated through some of the major gardens of Europe and it is of interest to repeat them here. It seems that the Imperial gardener in Kutais (in the Georgian S.S.R), whose name was Rögner, sent material to the St. Petersburg (Leningrad) Botanic Garden from whence it was further distributed, first as *Helleborus* sp. Abchasiae, after the province of Abkazia, then as *H. abchasicus*. In Germany, James Booth & Son of Hamburg appear to have received it first, and actually catalogued it in 1852, and it was sent on to the Berlin Botanic Garden to be described by A. Braun in the following year with the slightly altered spelling of *H. abschasicus*. This may have been an error, but whatever the explanation it seems best to revert to *abchasicus* without the softening 's' since the province name is pronounced with a guttural sound. Koch also noted that by 1857 it had reached Belgium and France, so the spread was quite rapid and one can see that by the late 19th century the plant must have been widely available for hybridisation purposes. Herbarium specimens show that it was being cultivated by the Rev. H.N. Ellacombe in 1877 from material actually sent to him by A. Braun, and Thomas Archer-Hind and Peter Barr were also in possession of it. These three were all important characters in the early history of the Hellebore hybrids in Britain, receiving new material from Europe and starting breeding programmes of their own. Some of the plants were probably imported direct from Leningrad, for the name *H. colchicus* appears frequently in literature and on herbarium specimens. This name was given by Regel to the stock which was growing in the St. Petersburg Botanic Garden, three years after it had already been described as *H. abchasicus* in Berlin.

The main point of distinction about *H. abchasicus* was that its flowers were dull purple, unlike those of the other related species in the *H. orientalis* complex in which they were cream, white or greenish. As an additional character it was noted that *H. abchasicus* (and *H. guttatus* which was described at the same time) possessed anthers which were emarginate, that is with a V-shaped dip at the apex, whereas the plants from Ulu Dağ in Turkey described as *H. antiquorum* and *H. olympicus* had minutely pointed anthers. Although this feature is not entirely reliable there does appear to be a tendency for the anthers of the coloured Caucasian plants to be elliptical and blunt while those of the western Turkish specimen are more narrowly oblong and often short-pointed.

Mention must be made here of an early flowering (often at Christmas) purple Hellebore to which, unfortunately, the name 'H. atrorubens of gardens' has become attached, although it is nothing to do with the true *H. atrorubens* of Waldstein & Kitaibel. In fact it represents a variant of *H. orientalis* subsp. *abchasicus*. It has leaves which are the shape of *H. orientalis* although they are rather less persistent through the winter than most forms, and they may only last until the flowering period before becoming brown. The flowers are of good size, of a medium purple suffused green, and they have green nectaries veined with dark red, a feature which is to be found in forms of *abchasicus*; sometimes the nectaries are wholly stained deep red-plum. A close inspection of the carpels reveals that they are completely free from each other, a clear indication of the plant's alliance with *H. orientalis* rather than *H. atrorubens* in which they are fused together at the base.

This 'atrorubens of gardens' has been cultivated for at least 100 years, for there are herbarium specimens of it at Kew dating from the 1870s, from the collections of Barr & Sons and Thomas Archer-Hind. One of the Barr specimens, under the name of *H. colchicus*, is dated December 1877, indicating the very early flowering time, while one of Archer-Hind's plants is labelled 'H. atrorubens = H. abchasicus'. I think it is highly likely that this was introduced into England from Leningrad or Berlin, in the second half of the 19th century, under the name of *H. colchicus*, perhaps with the epithet *atrorubens* attached as a sort of cultivar name; certainly there were other variants of *H. abchasicus* arriving at that period, bearing such names as 'Atroroseus', 'Ruber' and 'Colchicus Coccineus'.

This particular clone of *H. orientalis* subsp. *abchasicus* is an excellent garden plant and can be relied upon to flower in mid winter. It is said by some to be sterile, but its reluctance to produce seeds is probably caused by the cold weather during its flowering period, and the lack of pollinating insects. I have obtained small crops of seed by covering the plant with a cloche at flowering time; the resulting seedlings vary somewhat, as do the offspring of most *H. orientalis* variants.

To avoid confusion, and to shake off the misnomer of 'H. atrorubens', I now refer to my own plants as *H. orientalis* subsp. *abchasicus* 'Early Purple', an unromantic name but functional! It is well illustrated in the *Botanical Magazine*, Vol. 177, tab. 545 (1969) from a plant flowering on 12th December 1960 in the garden of Mr E. B. Anderson of Lower Slaughter, Gloucestershire.

Before leaving *H. abchasicus*, or *H. orientalis* subsp. *abchasicus* as I shall now call it, it is worth quoting from the *Flora of the U.S.S.R.* (1937) since it comments upon the fact that *H. abchasicus* hybridises with *H. orientalis* (which is referred to as *H. caucasicus*). 'In areas of W. Transcaucasia, where *H. caucasicus* and *H. abchasicus* occupy a common habitat, plants have been found with unusually varied flower coloration. Side by side were encountered specimens with flowers coloured dark purple, red, pale green, greenish white with a pink edge, white with a reddish tinge, etc. Most of these are probably of hybrid origin.'

H. guttatus was described by A. Braun and F. Sauer in 1853 from material sent to the Berlin Botanic Garden. K. Koch relates (in Schiffner, 1889) that he first found it in 1837 in woods near Tiflis and, on account of the very large flowers, called it *H. macranthus*; this was later changed to *H. grandiflorus* in Ruprecht's *Flora Caucasi* (1869), but neither of the names appear to have been validly published and are of no consequence. Living material collected by a Mr Frick near the former German town of Helenendorf (near the present city of Kirovabad) in the Caucasus was sent to St. Petersburg (Leningrad), then to M. Ad. Haage of Erfurt from whence it eventually reached Berlin via the University gardener Friedrich Sauer, who with Braun gave it the rather apt name of *H. guttatus*, referring to the red-spotted white flowers. During its travels it also acquired the name *H. intermedius* from Charles Morren of Gand (Ghent), Belgium, and was attractively illustrated as such in the *Annals of the Belgian Royal Agricultural and Botanical Society* for 1845. This name, although earlier than *H. guttatus*, cannot be utilised since *H. intermedius* had already been used twice by other authors for two entirely different plants.

H. orientalis subsp. *guttatus* has large creamy-white flowers, usually greenish towards the centre and spotted to varying degrees with reddish-purple. As mentioned above, under *H. orientalis* subsp. *abchasicus*, the anthers are usually blunt with a v-shaped notch at the apex. In cultivation this has been hybridized with subsp. *abchasicus* and subsp. *orientalis*, as well as with other species, resulting in a myriad of different forms, some so densely blotched as to form an almost solid purple-red eye in the centre. This probably reached England at much the same time, in the 19th century, as *H. abchasicus*, since there are herbarium specimens in existence of Archer-Hind's 'guttatus hybrids', raised at his garden at Coombe Fishacre in Devon during that period.

Following Alexander Braun's work in the 1850s there was undoubtedly much activity in the breeding of Hellebores but little development in the botanical classification of the species. J.G. Baker reviewed the genus in the *Gardeners' Chronicle* of 1877 and it is interesting to note that he regarded all the Caucasian and Turkish Hellebores as forms of *H. orientalis* but also included some of the Balkan species such as *H. odorus* and *H. atrorubens* under this name. He indicated that *guttatus* and *abchasicus* were not known to him as living plants at that time.

It was Dr Victor Schiffner of Prague University who provided the standard work on the genus, bringing together a mass of information and coupling this with his own studies to produce a fine monograph in 1889. Unfortunately he decided to provide a new name for the Hellebore from the Black Sea region, calling it *H. kochii*, with the explanation that Lamarck's *H. orientalis* was insufficiently well-defined to enable it to be used. However, he did consider it well-defined enough for it to be placed in synonymy under *H. kochii*! The grounds for rejecting *H. orientalis* are not strong and it is in fact *H. kochii* which becomes the synonym. Schiffner's *H. kochii* had two varieties, var. *hirtus*, in which the large leaves were hairy on the underside, and var. *glaber* with smaller, almost hairless, leaves. Hairiness, however, in *H. orientalis* appears to be a very variable feature and I am of the opinion that these varieties are not worthy of recognition. In Schiffner's treatment of this complex *H. abchasicus* and *H. guttatus* were maintained as species and, together with the creamy-coloured *H. kochii*, were distinguished from *H. antiquorum* and *H. olympicus* by their rounded, often emarginate anthers. *H. antiquorum* and *H. olympicus*, both with pointed anthers, were separated from each other by colour, white in *H. olympicus* and dull pinkish-red or pale pinkish-purple in *H. antiquorum*, and by the anthers being less strongly pointed in *H. olympicus*. The strength of the purplish colouring is probably an overstatement, for Braun originally described *H. antiquorum* as changing from white to purplish, a very frequent occurrence in the white or creamy-flowered Hellebores. As mentioned above, there is little evidence for maintaining *H. antiquorum* and *H. olympicus* and these should join *H. kochii* as synonyms of *H. orientalis*.

Over the years, following on from Schiffner's work, various other names were given to *H. orientalis*, including N. Busch's *H. casta-diva* (Busch, 1903) into which he curiously incorporated *H. kochii* and *H. abchasicus* as colour variants at subspecies rank, but kept *H. guttatus* as a separate species. The other major monographer, Dr E. Ulbrich, in his survey of the genus in 1938 did recognise *H. orientalis* Lam. as the valid name for the 'Pontic Hellebore' but he too maintained the dubiously distinct *H. antiquorum* and *H. olympicus* on account of their supposedly somewhat pointed anthers. *H. abchasicus* and *H. guttatus* were also recognised.

Perhaps one of the most entertaining approaches to the classification of the variants of *H. orientalis* came in 1939 when A.A. Kolakovski described a new species, *H. polychromus* (= 'many colours'). Many species were reduced to synonymy, including *H. abchasicus*, *H. caucasicus*, *H. guttatus*, *H. kochii* and *H. orientalis*, in spite of the fact that these were all valid names, pre-dating his own *H. polychromus*! Ten varieties of *H. polychromus* were described, only one of which, *guttatus*, utilised an existing epithet. Thus, varietal names such as *sanguineus*, *roseus*, *roseo-virens*, *flavo-virens*, *albo-virens*, *zebrinus*, *roseo-punctatus* and *nervosus* came into being, based on the flower colour and to some extent on the shade of green of the nectaries. A.A. Grossheim in *Flora Kavkaza* (1950) took up these varieties in his own work, but not as varieties of *H. polychromus*, instead he re-distributed them as varieties of *H. caucasicus* and *H. abchasicus*. There is little value in maintaining any of these names but their descriptions do serve to give an indication of the great range of variations of the Hellebores which occur in the Caucasus.

It is of interest to note that P.H. Davis in *Flora of Turkey* (1965) reduced all the above mentioned Turkish and Caucasian variants to synonymy under *H. orientalis* with the comment that 'The specimens from Lazistan [NE Turkey] tend to be less hairy than those from the more westerly part of the range, and are sometimes treated as *H. caucasicus* A. Br. However, intermediates between the 2 extremes are frequent. *H. orientalis* must be treated in the broad sense; it has been much divided on characters of sepal colour and the presence or absence of an apiculus on the anthers. These characters are correlated neither with each other nor with geography.'

To summarise, my own opinion is that there is only one species of Hellebore occurring in the region immediately to the south and east of the Black Sea, *H.*

orientalis. For practical purposes, two of its multitude of variants are worth recognising and, since they occur in certain areas within the whole range of the species, should be given subspecies status; these are subsp. *abchasicus* and subsp. *guttatus*.

Cultivation

H. orientalis presents few problems for the gardener and is, by and large, a very easily cultivated, very hardy, long-lived plant. It appears to do well in heavy clay soils through to light sandy ones, acid or alkaline, providing that it is not too hot and dry in summer, and not waterlogged in winter. Having stressed how tolerent it is I should add that the best collections of *H. orientalis* varieties I have seen are on fairly heavy alkaline soils in semi-shade and these conditions represent the nearest approximation to its natural habitat, although in parts of the Black Sea area it can certainly be found in association with acid indicating plants such as *Rhododendron luteum* and *R. ponticum*. Although dappled shade is perhaps the ideal, plants of *H. orientalis* will take full sun if there is enough moisture in the soil in the summer to stop them from wilting. In dry spells they are among the first plants to begin to look miserable and if they stay in this stressed state for long periods will almost certainly not flower well the following spring. The soil should be deeply cultivated with plenty of well-rotted organic matter worked in; this will automatically improve the drainage and aeration of the soil and lead to better water-retention in dry weather. Slow-release fertilizers certainly improve vigour and these are best given in spring when growth rate is at a maximum.

Large plants of *H. orientalis* can be moved perfectly satisfactorily if a large root ball is taken. They can also be divided, down to single crowns if so desired, but these smaller divisions will take at least two seasons to form reasonably strong plants (see also the general chapter on Propagation). Propagation by seed is a simple matter, providing that the seed is not stored dry for more than a few weeks. Seedlings often appear thickly around the parent plants, germinating in the autumn, so these can be lifted and potted or planted out separately in spring. If seeds are gathered they are best kept in a polythene bag with some moist tissue paper until sowing time, but if possible it is better to sow immediately they are ripe and keep the pots watered through summer, when germination should occur in the following autumn or winter. Seedlings may well not come true from seed since *H. orientalis* varieties will hybridise very readily and bees are usually very active on warm days in spring to encourage this. However, if cross-pollination is prevented then I find that the seedlings are likely to be fairly uniform. Seedlings usually take at least 2 years to produce flowers but it is possible, with ideal conditions and plenty of feeding, to get a flower stem in 1 year from germination, the flowers may however not show their true character until the next year.

H. orientalis Lamarck, Encycl. Méth. 3: 96 (1789).
Type: Turkey, 'Pont-Euxin (la mer Noire), and sur-tout au pied du Mont Olympe en Asie'. (specimen not traced).

Three subspecies are recognised:-

H. orientalis subsp. *abchasicus*. This
is an early-flowering form, often
erroneously known as 'H. atrorubens
of gardens'.

H. orientalis hybrids showing a range of colours and forms

H. orientalis hybrid raised by Elizabeth Strangman

H. orientalis hybrids in Mrs Helen Ballard's garden

One of Helen Ballard's blue-black
hybrids

A *H. orientalis* subsp. *guttatus*
selection

A very rounded flower of a *H. orientalis*
hybrid from Helen Ballard

'Orion' from Jim Archibald, with
contrasting purple nectaries

A yellow seedling from Helen Ballard

A fine white *H. orientalis* selection by
Elizabeth Strangman

A good pink *H. orientalis* hybrid raised
by Elizabeth Strangman

(a) subsp. *orientalis*

Synonyms

H. officinalis Salisb. in Trans. Linn. Soc. 8: 305 (1809)

H. olympicus Lindley in Bot. Reg. 14: misc. 113 (1841)

H. antiquorum A. Braun in Index Seminum Hort. Berol. 1853, appendix: 23 (1853)

H. caucasicus A. Braun in Index Seminum Hort. Berol. 1853, appendix: 24 (1853)

H. ponticus A. Braun in Index Seminum Hort. Berol. 1853, appendix: 24 (1853)

H. caucasicus var. *pallidus* Regel, Gartenflora 9: 192 (1860)

H. ibericus Stev. ex Rupr., Fl. Caucasi.: 287 (1869)

H. kochii Schiffner in Engl. Bot. Jahrb. 11: 108 (1889)

H. casta-diva Busch ssp. *kochii* (Schiffner) Busch in Fl. Cauc. Crit. 3, 3: addenda 226 (1903)

H. polychromus A.A. Kolak. in Not. Syst. Geog. Inst. Bot. Tphilisi. 5: 7 (1939)

Description

Glabrous or slightly hairy perennial herb up to 45 cm in height, with a tough rhizomatous rootstock. Leaves basal, overwintering, pedate with (5–)7–9(–11) segments, the central one undivided, leathery, deep green, glabrous or sparsely hairy beneath; leaf segments narrowly to broadly elliptic or oblanceolate, 10–25 cm long and up to 11 cm wide, the total leaf diameter up to 50 cm; margin coarsely serrate; petioles 15–36 cm long, green or purplish-suffused or spotted. Bracts rather large, the lower ones leaf-like with up to 5 segments, the upper ones sometimes ovate and undivided, equalling or overtopping the flowers. Inflorescences 15–35 cm tall with green or purple stained or spotted stems; sometimes simple and 1-flowered but usually branched with up to 4 flowers. Flowers usually (5.5–)6–7 cm diameter (cultivated selections may be up to 10 cm) unscented, nodding or almost facing outwards, saucer-shaped, white, cream or greenish-cream, often becoming faintly purplish-pink on the outside with age, carried on short stout curved pedicels which elongate to up to 5 cm in the fruiting stage; perianth segments broadly ovate or broadly elliptic, usually overlapping, obtuse to shortly acuminate, sometimes with undulate margins, usually 2.5–3.5 cm long, 1.8–3.3 cm wide; nectaries distinctly stalked, widely funnel-shaped, curved with an oblique or truncate mouth, slightly wavy or toothed at the margin, green; stamens numerous, erect at first then arching outwards, the outer ones first; anthers 1.5–3.5 mm long, oblong or elliptic, blunt and emarginate or minutely apiculate; carpels 4–7, completely free from each other; styles equalling or slightly exceeding the stamens, more or less straight. Follicles 1.5–2.5 cm long at maturity (excluding the style), narrowed abruptly at the base; seeds about 4–5 mm long, dark brown or blackish with a distinct ridge on one side.

Flowering time: February–May in the wild, January–April in cultivation.

Habitat: In deciduous woods and evergreen coniferous woods, and in grassy clearings, sea level to 2200 metres.

Distribution: NE. Greece; NW, N and NE. Turkey; USSR (C & W. Caucasia).

(b) subsp. *abchasicus* (A. Braun) B. Mathew

Type: USSR, Material cultivated at Berlin Botanic Garden, originating from W. Caucasus.

Synonyms

H. abschasicus A. Braun in Ind. Sem. Hort. Berol. 1853, appendix: 24 (1853).
   H. abascius Passerini, Piant. Nuove: 11 (1855).
H. colchicus Regel in Bull. Acad. St. Petersb.: 403 (1856)
H. caucasicus var. *colchicus* (Regel) Regel, Gartenfl. 9: 193, t. 293 (1860).
H. caucasicus var. *abchasicus* (A. Br.) Regel, Gartenfl. 9: 193 (1860).
H. caucasicus var. *abchasica* (A. Br.) Regel, Ind. Sem. Hort. Petrop.: 43 (1860).
H. caucasicus var. *cholchica* Regel in Ind. Sem. Hort. Petrop.: 43 (1860).
H. porphyromelas A. Br. & Bouché in Ind. Sem. Hort. Berol. 1862 appendix: 83 (1862).
H. casta-diva subsp. *abchasicus* (A. Br.) Busch in Kuznetzov, Busch & Fomin, Flora Caucasica Critica 3, 3: addenda 223 (1903).

Description

Very similar to subsp. *orientalis* (above) but flowers strongly suffused reddish-purple, sometimes also finely spotted darker purple on a purple ground; nectaries often darker purple or purple-streaked on a green ground; anthers blunt or rounded and emarginate.

Flowering time: April in the wild, January–April in cultivation.

Habitat: In woods and scrub.

Distribution: USSR, W. Caucasus.

(c) subsp. *guttatus* (A. Braun & Sauer) B. Mathew

Type: USSR, material cultivated at Berlin Botanic Garden, originally collected in the Caucasus.

Synonyms

H. guttatus A. Braun & Sauer in Ind. Sem. Hort. Berol. 1853, appendix: 24 (1853).
H. intermedius Morren in Ann. de Gand 1: 474, t. 44 (1845).
H. caucasicus var. *guttatus* (A. Br. & Sauer) Regel, Gartenfl. 9: 1860: 192 (1860)
H. caucasicus var. *guttata* (A. Br. & Sauer) Regel in Ind. Sem. Hort. Petrop. 1860: 43 (1860).
H. grandiflorus Koch ex Ruprecht, Fl. Caucasi: 32 (1869).
H. polychromus var. *guttatus* (A. Br. & Sauer) Kolak. in Not. Syst. Geog. Inst. Bot. Tphilisi. 5: 7 (1939).

Description

Very similar to subsp. *orientalis* (above) but flowers spotted red-purple on a whitish ground; anthers blunt or rounded, emarginate.

Flowering time: March–April.
Habitat: Woods.
Distribution: USSR, C & E. Caucasus.

7 *Helleborus cyclophyllus*

This attractive large green-flowered Hellebore from Greece, Bulgaria and southern Yugoslavia is one of the best contenders when searching for the true Black Hellebore of the ancient Greek physicians since it is the only species to occur in the particular sites which they mention. The other candidate is *H. orientalis*, a related species from western and northern Turkey, which would doubtless also have been known to them. Like all Hellebores the roots of both these species are blackish, especially when dried, and it is this colour which is reputed to have given rise to the name, although 'black' might well be a reference to its toxic properties or to the sinister diseases which the drug is reputed to have cured. It seems fairly likely that *H. cyclophyllus* was known to the herbalists some 2200 years or more before Alexander Braun gave it the name by which we know it today. Braun actually described it in 1862 as a variety of *H. viridis*, giving the origin rather vaguely as Greece, and using the epithet *cyclophyllus* because the outline of the leaf was roughly circular. Five years later Edmund Boissier gave it specific status and was more precise about its native haunts, mentioning Mt. Parnassus, Mt. Helicon, Mt. Olenos and Euboea, the first two of which were classical localities for collecting the medicinal Black Hellebore.

From its near relative *H. orientalis*, *H. cyclophyllus* is most obviously distinguished by having green flowers with a distinctive scent, rather similar to that of *Ribes sanguineum* or to Blackcurrant. Some people find this agreeable whilst others dislike it and liken the smell to tom cats. Both of these species have carpels which are free from each other right to the base whereas in all the other Balkan species, including *H. odorus* (which resembles *H. cyclophyllus*), the carpels are fused together at the base for about 2 mm or so. The large leaves of *H. cyclophyllus* are silvery-hairy on the undersides, especially when young, and they do not usually overwinter, dying away in the autumn months. However some forms such as those from Corfu are less prone to losing their leaves so this cannot be taken as being a hard and fast rule. In *H. orientalis* and *H. odorus* the leaves are very tough and leathery and normally last right through the winter until new ones appear just after flowering time. Even with *H. orientalis* however there is a tendency for the leaves of some forms of the Caucasian subsp. *abchasicus* to die away during the winter. I have dealt with the question of the differences between

H. cyclophyllus and *H. odorus* at greater length under the latter species, but I should perhaps repeat that these two are very closely allied and merge in their features, perhaps due to hybridisation in the parts of their ranges where they meet. *H. cyclophyllus* may be regarded as a true member of the Mediterranean flora whereas *H. odorus* is a more northerly-occurring plant of inland areas bordering on the Sub-Mediterranean and Central European climatic zones (Polunin & Walters 1985). In Greece, *H. cyclophyllus* is a common plant on the mainland mountains and is also present in Corfu, Euboea and the northern Peloponnese. Northwards it extends into Albania, Yugoslavian Macedonia and southern Bulgaria. In south-eastern Yugoslavia I have seen areas in which it meets *H. torquatus* with obvious intermediates, some with dissected leaves and green flowers tinged with brown-purple and others with the large, less-divided leaves of *H. cyclophyllus* but with purplish flowers.

As with most species, *H. cyclophyllus* is somewhat variable although it has not received the attentions of 'splitters' and there is no great proliferation of infraspecific taxa such as we find in some of the other Balkan Hellebores. There is a certain amount of variation in the number of segments to the leaves, usually between 9 and 14, whereas *H. odorus* varies between 7 and 11. The flowers are frequently a strong yellowish-green and are of good size, 5–7 cm in diameter, sometimes carried in a pendent position but quite often held so that they face outwards displaying the stamens. Since it will cross freely with *H. orientalis* these features make it an ideal choice as a parent in trying to breed a race of yellowish Hellebores and it has in fact been used by several people for this purpose. Some of the best yellows are derived from this species although other good ones have been derived from *H. odorus* and *H. multifidus* variants.

As a garden subject, *H. cyclophyllus* is, when growing well, a striking plant with its large clear green flowers, and the leaves are not unattractive, being silvery-hairy as they push through the ground in early spring.

Cultivation

H. cyclophyllus requires a sheltered position with rather more sun than *H. orientalis*, for it is typically a plant of open dryish hillsides or slightly shaded areas. I find that it is liable to be damaged during severe frosts although there is some variation in hardiness depending upon the origin of a particular individual and plants from the higher altitudes are undoubtedly tougher than those from near sea level. It is also susceptible to the leaf spot diseases and is one of the first to succumb during wet winters.

H. cyclophyllus (A. Braun) Boissier, Fl. Orient. 1: 61 (1867)

Type: from Greece (specimen not traced).

Synonym

H. viridis var. *cyclophyllus* A. Braun in Ind. Sem. Hort. Berol., appendix: 14 (1862).

Description

Perennial herb (20–)25-40 cm in height at flowering time; rhizome tough with
stout roots. Basal leaves not usually overwintering, thick and leathery, pedate
with the lateral leaflets each deeply divided into 5–7 lobes, the central one divided
or undivided, giving a total of about 9–14 segments per leaf; leaflets and their
segments elliptic or oblanceolate, up to 20 cm long and up to 5 cm wide, densely
hairy on the underside, usually over the whole surface but sometimes only on the
stout prominent veins; margin coarsely serrate; petioles up to 40 cm long, green.
Bracts rather large, often equalling or overtopping the flowers, divided into 3–5
coarsely serrate segments. Inflorescences usually widely branched and carrying up
to 7 flowers. Flowers 5–7 cm in diameter (later flowers are often smaller than the
first), scented, facing outwards or nodding, flattish or saucer-shaped, yellowish-
green, carried on stout pedicels up to 2.5 cm long; perianth segments equal or
subequal, overlapping, broadly ovate, broadly elliptical or suborbicular, obtuse
or rounded, usually 2.5–3.5 cm long, 2–2.8 cm wide; nectaries distinctly stalked,
widely funnel-shaped, curved with a slightly oblique or truncate mouth, slightly
toothed or wavy at the margin, green; stamens numerous, erect or suberect,
anthers 1.5–2.5 mm long; carpels 3–5(–6), free from each other at the base and
sometimes shortly stalked; styles usually exceeding the stamens, straight or
slightly curved. Follicles 1.5–2 cm long at maturity (excluding the style),
narrowed abruptly at the base; seeds 4–5 mm long, dark brown with a distinct
but not markedly swollen ridge on one side.

Flowering time March–May(–June) in the wild, January–March in cultivation.

Habitat Dryish deciduous woods (*Quercus, Carpinus, Corylus*) and scrub,
sometimes in open grassland, often on calcareous formations but not solely so,
30–2000 metres.

Distribution Greece, widespread on the mainland, Euboea, Corfu and N.
Peloponnese; S. Yugoslavia; S. Bulgaria, Albania.

8 *Helleborus purpurascens*

H. purpurascens, in its best forms, is one of the most charming of all Hellebores
but it is very variable and can conversely be so drab and uninteresting as to be
scarcely worth cultivating. The most attractive and typical variants are those with
saucer-shaped flowers of a dull purplish-violet overlaid with a greyish 'bloom',

but the colour varies from a reddish-purple through shades of subdued violet to a dirty greenish-brown. E.B. Anderson likened the colour of the form he knew to that of a dove or pigeon on the outside of the perianth segments and emerald green on the interior. The inside of the flower is however not necessarily green and may be of a similar colour to the exterior. The excellent form depicted here by Mary Grierson has been in cultivation for a very long time and was given to me by the Royal Botanic Garden, Edinburgh, many years ago.

The main characteristics of *H. purpurascens* are the cup- or saucer-shaped purple flowers, which open almost as soon as they push through the ground, and the distinctive leaves with their divided leaflets all radiating from the top of the petiole to give a nearly circular outline. The illustration in the *Botanical Magazine*, plate 3170 (1832) is rather poor and unnatural in appearance but it does show the overall facies of this lovely Hellebore, as does the painting in Volume 2 of Waldstein and Kitaibel's *Plantarum Rariorum Hungariae* of 1812. The latter shows clearly the palmate leaves with their divided leaflets and the large greyish-purple flowers on short stems. The leaf shape of *H. purpurascens* is thus quite different in appearance from the strictly pedate arrangement of *H. atrorubens* and *H. torquatus* and it was referred to by Schiffner as 'handförmig' to distinguish it from the 'fussförmig' shape found in these two related species. In *H. purpurascens* the leaves do not remain green through the winter and when the new ones appear in spring they can be seen to be downy on the underside. In weak specimens each leaflet may have only two divisions but in vigorous plants there may be five or six, giving as many as thirty segments to the whole leaf. A typical leaf of *H. atrorubens*, on the other hand, has only the lateral leaflets divided and the central one is undivided. In *H. torquatus* the leaves are much-divided but here the arrangement is also pedate so that there is usually no difficulty in distinguishing them from those of *H. purpurascens*. Typical examples of the three are shown in our line drawings on page 31, but it must be borne in mind that each species varies in the leaf shape and amount of division, partly depending upon the vigour of the individual plant. (See page 148).

Although the first flowers of *H. purpurascens* open while their stems are very short, flowering continues over a lengthy period during which time they elongate and may be up to 25 cm in height by the time the last blooms have faded. In general it can be said that the flowers are rather larger than those of *H. atrorubens* and *H. torquatus*, at about 5–7 cm diameter, with broad blunt segments but here again it is variable and forms with smaller, narrower, more pointed segments can be somewhat different in appearance. A plant given to me by John Marr, collected near Cluj in Romania, represents one such form with smallish flowers in reddish-purple, produced slightly later than those of the Edinburgh form mentioned above, and they are on taller stems, but it does have the tell-tale palmate leaves of *H. purpurascens*. Other plants of this species which I have grown from wild collected seed have turned out to be rather less attractive in shades of brownish-purple or greenish-brown but they are early-flowering and open as soon as they push through the soil and so do have a certain amount of garden value.

Some of the forms of *H. purpurascens* have been given names and these are worth recording for interest's sake, although they are of little horticultural importance since they do not register variation for aesthetic reasons but are mainly concerned with leaf characters:

(a) **forma *asperus* Simk.** Leaf segments roughly-hairy on the veins on the underside.

(b) **forma *baumgartenii*** (Kov.) Nyár. (Syn. *H. purpurascens* var. *baumgartenii* Kovats; *H. p.* var. *subflagellatus* Schur). Leaf segments narrowly lanceolate with the primary segments sessile or subsessile. It has been suggested that this has arisen through hybridisation with *H. multifidus* but this seems unlikely since the two do not overlap in the wild.

(c) **forma *dniesterensis*** Zapal. Smallish flowers with perianth segments 2–2.5 cm long; leaves slightly smaller than is usual for the species.

(d) **forma *glabrescens*** Simk. Leaf segments with the veins beneath becoming glabrous with age.

(e) **forma *grossedentatus*** Nyár. Leaf segments with coarse teeth 5–10 mm long.

(f) **forma *nanus*** Zapal. Plant only 18 cm in height at maturity, stems with one flower.

(g) **forma *quadriflorus*** Zapal. Stems with four flowers. I imagine this and f. *nanus* represent strong and weak specimens.

(h) **forma *subdivisus*** Zapal. Leaflets undivided, a rather rare occurrence and not a variant I have encountered personally.

(i) **forma *tuzsonii*** Andréanszky. Leaf segments narrowly lanceolate, the primary ones narrowed at the base into a stalk 1–2 cm long (as opposed to the sessile ones of f. *baumgartenii*, for example).

(j) **forma *typicus*.** The typical form which should in modern nomenclature be called f. *purpurascens*.

(k) **forma *viridiflorus*** (Schur) Nyár. (Syn. *H. p.* var. *viridiflorus* Schur) Flowers greenish.

In the wild *H. purpurascens* occurs in woods and thickets and has been recorded growing with such plants as *Daphne mezereum*, *Asarum europaeum*, *Anemone nemorosa*, *Crocus vernus* (*C. heuffelianus*), *Erythronium dens-canis*, *Isopyrum thalictrioides*, *Pulmonaria officinalis* and *Dentaria bulbifera*. It is a very widespread plant in Romania, except for the eastern lowland part of the country, and extends northwards into USSR in the Carpathians through the western Ukraine, into the extreme south eastern corner of Poland and eastern Czechoslovakia; westwards, it occurs in northern and central Hungary but as far as I can ascertain does not enter Yugoslavia, the records of it there probably referring to *H. atrorubens* or *H. torquatus*. The recent *Analitička Flora Jugoslavije* (1973) does not acknowledge its existence in the country. Thus *H. purpurascens* has a distribution which is distinct from that of the other two Balkan purple-flowered species, *H. atrorubens* and *H. torquatus*, occurring to the east of the former and to the northeast of the latter.

Cultivation

H. purpurascens is, in my experience, one of the most susceptible species to the leaf spot diseases, which often attack the flowers and their stems as well as the leaves, completely ruining the display during mild damp winters. The control measures given on page 160 are a help but as an additional precaution in wet weather when the plant is in bloom I usually cover it with an open-ended cloche. This appears to deter the spread of the disease by keeping the flowers dry. Some forms seem to be more resistant than others and the Romanian one collected by

Dr John Marr does not suffer nearly as badly as the one I received from Edinburgh.

The best place to grow *H. purpurascens* seems to be in slight shade in a well-drained humus-rich soil. No hellebore likes the conditions to be excessively acid or damp so, if available, leafmould or well-rotted garden compost should be used rather than peat. It has grown well for me planted on a raised 'log garden' where the soil behind the logs had been made up with leafmould and moss peat, giving a cool root run and at the same time free drainage.

Seeds are not produced very freely, even when the flowers are hand pollinated, and I assume that this is because of its habit of flowering very early when temperatures are usually rather low. In its eastern European home it stays dormant longer and flowers in the spring when the day temperatures are likely to be higher.

H. purpurascens Waldst. & Kit., Pl. Rar. Hung. 2: 105, tab. 101 (1802/1803).

Type: Hungary, Matra Mts., Vertes Mts. (?specimens in Prague)

Synonyms

H. viridis var. *purpurascens* (W. & K.) Neilreich, Aufz. Ung. and Slav. beob. Gefässpflanzen: 242 (1866)

H. hunfalvyanus Kan. var. *purpurascens* (W. & K.) Kan., in Hunfalvys ung. Pflanzengeogr.

Description

Perennial herb, usually about 5–20 cm in height at flowering time, the stems elongating somewhat in the fruiting stage; rhizome tough with stout roots. Basal leaves not overwintering, rather thick and leathery, palmate, usually with 5 primary leaflets, each of these deeply divided into 2–6 lanceolate segments (rarely some undivided), the whole leaflet 10–20 cm long with the segments 1–4 cm wide, wedge-shaped at the base, acute at the apex, hairy on the underside, sometimes only on the stout prominent veins; margin coarsely serrate; petioles 15–25 cm long, green or purplish-suffused. Bracts rather small, the lowest subtending the first branch (if branched at all) of the inflorescence with a widely winged petiole and 3–5 small leaf-like divisions, or rarely entire and scale-like, the upper ones subtending flowers deeply divided into 3–5 toothed segments, shorter than to slightly overtopping the flower. Inflorescences appearing before the leaves, usually 5–15 cm when the first flowers open but elongating during flowering to 15–25(–30) cm by the fruiting stage. Flowers about 5–7 cm diameter, unscented, nodding, cup-shaped, (1–)2–3(–4) per stem, carried on pedicels 0.5–2 cm long, purplish-violet, reddish-purple, brownish or rarely almost green, usually glaucous on the exterior, the inside the same colour as the outside or green; perianth segments equal or subequal, overlapping, broadly ovate or broadly elliptic, obtuse or sometimes subacute at the apex, 2–3.5 cm long, 1.5–2.4(–3) cm wide; nectaries 15–20, distinctly stalked, widely funnel-shaped, curved with an oblique uneven-toothed margin, green or purplish; stamens numerous, erect or suberect, anthers 1.5–2.5 mm long; carpels 5–7, sometimes up to 9, very short joined at the base; styles equalling or exceeding the stamens, straight or slightly curved. Follicles about 2 cm long at maturity (excluding the persistent style), each narrowed abruptly at the base; seeds ellipsoid, about 4 mm long, blackish-brown with a distinct ridge on one side.

Flowering time March–April in the wild, January–March in cultivation.

Habitat Light woodland or at the margins of woods and spinneys, often in sandy and alluvial soils, 180–650 metres.

Distribution Widespread in Romania, C. & N. Hungary, E. Czechoslovakia, S.E. Poland, W. Ukraine.

9 *Helleborus torquatus*

H. torquatus is one of the three purple-flowered species from the Balkans and is somewhat better-known in gardens than either of the other two since it has been used in hybridisation to introduce some of the deep blackish-purple colours into the *H. orientalis* hybrids. Although it is a most attractive plant in its own right it has, as a parent, given us some very beautiful hybrids. Recent examples include Eric Smith's 'Pluto' and Helen Ballard's 'Blue Wisp', and doubtless it played a part in the breeding of some of the darker cultivars of the more distant past, like 'Black Knight' and 'Ballard's Black'.

Exactly when *H. torquatus* came into cultivation is not entirely clear but it seems that it may have been known at least as early as the 1850s in the Berlin Botanic Garden under the name *H. intermedius*. This latter species was described by Host in 1831 and has been interpreted as being a naturally-occurring hybrid between *H. atrorubens* and *H. dumetorum* but there appears to be no firm foundation for this and, although it is difficult to be sure, it seems more likely that it is a variant of the species which was named *H. torquatus* in 1884, then *H. serbicus* in 1906 and *H. multifidus* subsp. *serbicus* in 1961. Although *H. intermedius* Host (1831) is the earliest name, under the International Code of Nomenclature it is unacceptable since the epithet had already been used by Gussone. The fact that *H. intermedius* Gussone (1826) is a synonym of *H. bocconei* (1823) has no bearing on the matter and the epithet cannot be re-used for another species.

Thomas Archer-Hind provided the name *H. torquatus* in *The Garden* of 8 March 1884, placing it in the 'Group Acaules, non-persistent' [i.e. the leaves do not overwinter]. His notes read, 'the smallest of the purples; purple inside and out; remarkable for the manner in which the flower stands at right angles from its short stem, and for the white collar round its neck, from which feature I gave the name on finding the plant many years ago in an old garden'. The history of this particular plant is recorded in greater detail in *The Garden* of 13 December 1884 in an article describing Archer-Hind's garden at Coombe Fishacre near Newton

Abbot in Devonshire. The author of this article writes that Archer-Hind 'only knew of one plant of it many years ago, in the Botanic Garden at Cambridge. On visiting the gardens one autumn, when Mr Mudd was the curator, he found considerable alterations in progress, and this Hellebore had been covered up and turfed over. On his attention being drawn to it, Mr Mudd had a search made, and luckily the plant was found, and a piece of it given to Mr Archer-Hind. This is the origin of the present stock. It was named *torquatus* because of a white ring which encircles the neck of the flower' [the latin name means provided or adorned with a collar]. The list of plants cultivated at Cambridge Botanic Garden in 1850 included *H. intermedius* so it is possible that this was the same stock as that referred to by Archer-Hind and re-named by him *H. torquatus* in 1884.

H. torquatus was also to be found at about this time in the nursery trade, but whether this was a result of Archer-Hind's rescue mission or quite independently we shall never know. It was offered in the 1889 nursery catalogue of Barr & Sons, described as a 'very fine dwarf species with beautiful dove-coloured flowers'. Interestingly, this list also includes *H. intermedius*, which was described as 'outside dove-purple, inside green', so it would appear that at least two forms of this species were in cultivation at the time, under different names.

By a fortunate series of events I am able to link together various pieces of history associated with *H. torquatus*. In the mid 1960s I assisted Sir Frederick Stern in his chalk garden at Highdown in Sussex, and one of the treasures he showed me was a plant of *H. torquatus* which he said was a part of the Archer-Hind stock. Little did I realise that this was such an historically important individual, for it is probably the nearest I will ever be to seeing a type specimen of *H. torquatus* since there appears to be no dried material of Archer-Hind's plant in existence. To me, this plant undoubtedly belonged to the same species as I had seen in southern Yugoslavia in 1963 and 1965, although it was clear that there was not just one form of *H. torquatus* but many, differing in stature, flower colour and shape and in the degree of leaf division. Before this, in 1959 and 1960, I had the good fortune to work at the Ingwersen's nursery at Gravetye near East Grinstead and there, beneath a magnificent beech tree, grew a plant of *H. torquatus* which had been collected by W.E. Th. Ingwersen in 1929 from Mt. Koprivnik in Montenegro. This was, at the time of its introduction, an exciting and important find since the origin of *H. torquatus* was unknown and it was thought to have been lost to cultivation. When I asked Mr Walter Ingwersen about this plant he said that it was found quite by chance in a thunderstorm when he was seeking privacy during a bout of diarrhoea, not the most romantic of plant collecting stories but extremely fortunate for British horticulture! Plants of the 'Ingwersen *torquatus*' reached various growers and undoubtedly some of the present very dark hybrids are the happy result of liaisons between this and the *H. orientalis* cultivars. Having seen a plant of Archer-Hind's form, the Ingwersen form, and several wild populations of *H. torquatus*, I am quite certain that these are all variants of the same species.

One slight puzzle is Archer-Hind's reference to a white collar around the neck of the flower. By 'neck' one would normally think of the outside of the flower where the sepals join the stalk, but in all the forms of *H. torquatus* which I have seen there has been no such 'collar'. Usually the outside of the sepals is a uniform purple colour right to the base, although sometimes there is a paler green ring surrounding the pedicel. One reference I have seen to *H. torquatus* describes the collar as being at the base of the sepals, without specifying inside or out, and it seems to me more likely that the white ring referred to is in fact on the inside. This paler zone is to be seen in some forms of *H. torquatus* and is sometimes carried through to its hybrid offspring, which display a white eye right in the centre of an otherwise dark flower; this is particularly visible in the late flowering stage when the stamens and nectaries have fallen, thus allowing a clear view of the centre.

As I have indicated above, *H. torquatus* is an extremely variable plant and, in addition, it seems that in the wild it hybridises with other species giving an apparently even greater range of variation. I have observed hybrid swarms between *H. torquatus* and *H. cyclophyllus* in Montenegro and almost certainly it crosses with *H. multifidus* in parts of western Yugoslavia. The most interesting variation from the gardener's viewpoint is in flower colour which may be purple to violet-black on the outside of the sepals, overlaid with a greyish bloom like black grapes, and it is this glaucous appearance which has caused several authors to describe the flowers as dove-coloured. The inner surfaces of the sepals may be the same colour as the outside, or paler purple and suffused with green, or sometimes plain clear green with no trace of purple, a variation which I personally find most attractive. Another variant, which seems to occur mainly in Croatia, has flowers which are dark on the outside and green within, but veined with dark purple as if blue-black ink has seeped through the main conducting vessels of the sepals (see colour plate on p. 106). This form, at least in the plant I have seen from the area, has pendent, rather conical flowers whereas those from farther south in Montenegro have flattish or saucer-shaped flowers which are often held facing outwards rather than downwards, although this is not a consistent feature. The name *H. croaticus* has been given to the more northerly-occurring plants but I cannot see any wholly reliable characters by which to distinguish these from the southern populations. Several variants of *H. croaticus* [and of *H. serbicus*] have been described at the rank of *forma*, differing from each other in the degree of leaf division and width of the individual segments. These are: *H. croaticus* f. *angustisectus* Martinis; *H. croaticus* f. *latisectus* Martinis; *H. croaticus* f. *polysectus* Martinis; *H. serbicus* f. *gočensis* Gajić (narrow segments); *H. serbicus* f. *latisectus* Gajić.

H. torquatus varies considerably in its leaf characters, mainly in the amount of dissection, but usually having somewhere between 15 and 25 segments which are distinctively long-tapering to an acute apex. As with the other two purple-flowered Balkan species, the leaves are winter-deciduous, the new ones appearing during the later stages of flowering. They are somewhat hairy beneath as in *H. purpurascens* but are pedately divided whereas those of the latter are more or less palmate. The *H. torquatus* populations from Yugoslavia have often been referred to as *H. purpurascens* but I rather doubt that this species, a more easterly and northerly occurring plant from Romania, Hungary and Czechoslovakia on into the Carpathian mountains of southern Poland and western Ukraine, is to be found in Yugoslavia at all. The flowers of *H. torquatus*, at about 4–5.5 cm diameter, are not generally as large as those of *H. purpurascens* in which they are usually 5–7 cm diameter, but there is an overlap in measurement. *H. atrorubens*, which occurs only in northern Yugoslavia, has glabrous, pedately divided leaves with fewer segments than those of *H. torquatus* and *H. purpurascens*. (see drawings pages 31 and 148).

Double forms of *H. torquatus* have been found in the wild. In 1971 Elizabeth Strangman found in Crna Gora (Montenegro) two good forms which she subsequently introduced into cultivation as 'Dido' and 'Aeneas'.

H. torquatus has an inland distribution in Yugoslavia, in Crna Gora (Montenegro), Bosnia and Hercegovina, western Serbia and Croatia, apparently not crossing the coastal ranges of mountains where *H. multifidus* is a common species, although it does seem to meet this at certain places giving rise to intermediate plants which may be taken to be of hybrid origin. *H. torquatus* is a plant of deciduous woodland, often to be found growing in damp places near streams in silty soil, although I have also seen it on rather drier banks of heavy soil in scrub.

Cultivation

H. torquatus is a fine garden plant, not difficult to cultivate in partial shade but it will also take full sun if grown in a humus-rich soil which is well-supplied with moisture in the early part of the year. The best plants I have are in heavy soil adjacent to the vegetable plot which means that it has received a lot of organic matter in the past, mainly in the form of leaves. *H. torquatus* is somewhat susceptible to the leaf spot diseases but it responds well to spraying with fungicide, as recommended in chapter 10.

H. torquatus Archer-Hind in *The Garden* 8 March 1884: 184 (1884).

Type: cultivated material of unstated origin; dried specimen not traced.

Synonyms

H. intermedius Host, Fl. Austriaca 2: 88 (1831).

H. serbicus Adamović in Magyar Bot. Lap. 5: 221 (1906).

H. odorus subsp. *multifidus* var. *violascens* (Beck) Hayek in Prodr. Fl. Pen. Balcan. 1: 299 (1927).

H. multifidus subsp. *serbicus* (Adamović) Merxmüller & Podlech in Fedde, Repert. Spec. Nov. 64: 5 (1961)

H. serbicus subsp. *malyi* Martinis in Suppl. Fl. Anal. Jugosl. 1: 14 (1973).

H. croaticus Martinis in Suppl. Fl. Anal. Jugosl. 1: 14 (1973).

Description

Perennial herb, usually 20–40 cm in height at flowering time; rhizome tough with stout roots. Basal leaves not overwintering, rather leathery when mature, pedate, usually with each of the leaflets, including the central one, deeply divided into 2–6 segments giving a total of (10–)15–25(–30), rarely the central one undivided; leaflets 10–17 cm long with their segments normally 1–3.5 cm wide, wedge-shaped at the base, long-tapering to an acute apex, hairy on the underside, sometimes only on the very stout prominent veins; margin coarsely serrate; petioles 15–25 cm long, green or purplish suffused. Bracts rather large, deeply divided into 3–5 narrow toothed segments, usually overtopping the flowers but sometimes vice versa when the flowers first open. Inflorescences appearing before the new leaves, usually 20–40 cm in height when the first flowers open but elongating during flowering to 40 cm by the fruiting stage. Flowers (3.5–)4–5.5(–6) cm diameter, unscented or rarely faintly clove-scented, held facing outwards and saucer-shaped to somewhat nodding and conical cup-shaped, (1–)2–5(–7) per stem, carried on pedicels 0.5–2 cm long; colour dark violet-purple and glaucous on the outside, inside the same colour, or green, or sometimes green veined with purple; perianth segments equal or subequal, slightly overlapping to more or less separated, ovate or elliptic, obtuse or subacute at the apex, (1.5–)2–2.8(–3.4) cm long, 0.9–2 cm wide; nectaries about 10–20, distinctly stalked, widely funnel-shaped, curved with an oblique uneven-toothed margin, green; stamens numerous, erect or suberect, anthers 1.5–2.5 mm long; carpels 3–5, very shortly joined at the base; styles equalling to much-exceeding the stamens, straight or slightly curved. Follicles 1.5–2 cm long at maturity (excluding the persistent style), each narrowed abruptly at the base; seeds ellipsoid, about 4 mm long, blackish-brown with a small but distinct ridge on one side.

Flowering time March–April in the wild, January–March in cultivation.

Habitat In light deciduous woodland or the margins of woods and thickets, often in clay soils or silty soils near streams, 300–2100 metres.

Distribution Yugoslavia, recorded in Croatia, Bosnia and Hercegovina, Crna Gora (Montenegro) and W. Serbia.

10 *Helleborus atrorubens*

It is unfortunate that this name has become firmly attached in the minds of gardeners to a very early large purple-flowered Hellebore ('*H. atrorubens* of gardens') which, although a superb and useful garden plant, is not entitled to the name. Further comments are made about this plant under *H. orientalis* on page 81, since it is a variant of that species.

 H. atrorubens was first described by Waldstein and Kitaibel in their *Plantarum Rariorum Hungariae* of 1812 and illustrated on page 271. The description and illustration indicate clearly that the leaves are glabrous beneath and are strictly pedate, with the leaflets broad and undivided, and the flowers are of a mediocre size. Thus it is fairly readily distinguished from *H. purpurascens* in which the leaves are pubescent beneath, have a palmate rather than pedate arrangement and possess divided leaflets; the flowers of the latter are generally larger than those of *H. atrorubens* and often have a glaucous 'bloom' on the exterior of the perianth segments. The third Balkan purple-flowered Hellebore, *H. torquatus*, may resemble *H. atrorubens* in flower characters, and it also has pedate leaves, but differs in that all the leaflets are divided, even the central one, and they are pubescent beneath. (See page 148).

 H. atrorubens as it occurs in the wild has medium sized unscented flowers about 4–5 cm in diameter, which are in various shades of violet on the exterior and are often green within. They are carried on tall stems, usually around 20–30 cm in height which may bear up to five flowers on fairly long branches. Thus it has a rather different appearance from *H. purpurascens* when in flower, since in the latter the flowers open while the stems are very short. Aesthetically the best forms are those with very dark violet flowers with a contrasting 'eye' of yellow stamens; this dark coloration sometimes spreads to the stems and foliage as well, giving the leaves an almost metallic sheen. It is a rare plant in cultivation, seen even less frequently than *H. purpurascens*, and although it has no greater ornamental value than the latter species it is nevertheless an interesting and attractive plant, worthy of a place in the garden.

The type locality of *H. atrorubens* is in the mountains of Croatia (this region appears to be its main stronghold) extending northwestwards into Slovenia: and it is clearly confined to northwest Yugoslavia. There is no evidence that it reaches Hungary or Romania so is in fact distinct in its distribution from *H. purpurascens*.

In *Flora Europaea* (1964) *H. atrorubens* was treated as a subspecies of the smaller green-flowered *H. dumetorum* which has a similar but more extensive distribution from southern Austria into Yugoslavia and eastwards to Hungary and Romania. There is no difficulty in recognising these two at a glance and I have therefore maintained them as species, since the distinguishing features between all these Balkan green and purple-flowered Hellebores are very slight and if one embarks on a course of merging species such as *H. dumetorum* and *H. atrorubens* there is little justification for maintaining several of the other species.

As with all Hellebore species there is considerable variation and the concept of a particular species is best based on what appears to be the norm, regarding the occasional 'odd' variants as mutants. *H. atrorubens* has its share of these abnormal variants and some of these have been given names, for which the status of *forma* seems appropriate. The typical form obviously takes the name of forma *atrorubens*.

(a) **forma *cupreus*** (Host) Martinis (*H. cupreus* Host) has coppery coloured flowers rather than violet.
(b) **forma *hircii*** Martinis (*H. intermedius* Hirc, not of Host). A variant in which the leaves have a few more segments than is normal, up to eleven or even rarely to fifteen.
(c) **forma *incisus*** Martinis has the leaf margins very coarsely toothed.

Cultivation
H. atrorubens appears to be a reasonably accommodating species in gardens and is very hardy, as one would expect from its area of distribution. It seems to thrive best in well drained semi-shaded situations and, like most species, is suited to alkaline soils. An appropriate site would be beneath or near deciduous trees or shrubs with a good humus content in the soil, preferably consisting of leafmould or rotted compost rather than peat. It can be propagated by seed but in the garden the chances of hybridisation with other related species are high unless steps are taken to prevent this.

H. atrorubens Waldst. & Kit. Pl. Rar. Hung. 3: 301, tab. 271 (1812).

Type: 'Habitat in sylvaticus & in fruticetis montanae Croatiae' (specimen in Prague?).

Synonyms

H. atropurpureus Schultes, Fl. Oester, ed. 2, 2: 103 (1814)

H. cupreus Host, Fl. Austr. 2: 87 (1831)

H. odorus var. *atrorubens* (W. & K.) Koch in Roehl, Deutschl. Fl. ed. 3, 4: 198 (1833)

H. officinalis var. *atrorubens* (W. & K.) Spach, Hist. Nat. Veg. 7: 317 (1839), partly.

H. viridis var. *atrorubens* (W. & K.) Kittel, Taschenbuch Fl. Deutschl. ed. 2: 243 (1844)

H. viridis var. *cupreus* (Host) Neilr., Aufz. Ung. Slavon.: 243 (1866)

H. hunfalvyanus var. *atrorubens* (W. & K.) Kanitz in Schulzer v. Mueggenb., Kanitz & Knapp, Pfl. Slabon.: 138 (1866)

H. hunfalvyanus var. *cupreus* (Host) Kanitz, loc. cit. 138

H. dumetorum subsp. *atrorubens* (W. & K.) Merxm. & Podl. in Feddes Repert. 64: 5 (1961)

Description

Glabrous perennial herb usually about 25–35 cm in height at flowering time, not elongating appreciably in the fruiting stage; rhizome tough with stout roots. Basal leaves rather thin in texture, not overwintering, pedate with the central leaflet undivided, the lateral ones divided into about 3–5 segments, thus making about 7–11 narrowly elliptic segments in all, completely glabrous, even on the veins beneath which are rather slender, not stout and prominent; the central leaflet is about 10–21 cm long, 2–2.5 cm wide, acute at the apex, wedge-shaped at the base; margins coarsely serrate; petioles 15–25 cm long, green or purplish suffused. Cauline leaves (bract leaves) equalling or slightly overtopping the flowers, deeply divided into 3–5 toothed segments. Inflorescence appearing before the leaves, usually 15–30 cm in height when the flowers open. Flowers (1–) 2–3(–5) per stem, carried on pedicels c. 1–2 cm long, deep violet, usually suffused green on the inside, unscented, held more or less horizontally, flattish or saucer-shaped, 4–5(–5.5) cm in diameter; perianth segments equal or subequal, not or only slightly overlapping, ovate, subacute or sometimes obtuse at the apex, 2–2.5(–2.7) cm long, 1.5–2.1 cm wide. Nectaries 15–20, distinctly stalked, widely funnel-shaped, curved with an oblique entire margin, green; stamens numerous, erect or suberect, anthers 1.5–3 mm long; carpels 5–6, shortly fused at the base; styles nearly straight or curved, often with a crook at the apex. Follicles about 2–2.5 cm long at maturity (excluding the persistent style) narrowed abruptly at the base; seeds ellipsoid, about 4–5 mm long, dark brown with a distinct ridge on one side.

Flowering time March–April in the wild, February–March in cultivation.

Habitat Dryish hillsides in spinneys and the margins of Oak and Beech woods, usually on limestone formations, up to 1500 m.

Distribution N.W. Yugoslavia in Croatia and Slovenia.

11 *Helleborus dumetorum*

Although the smallest-flowered of all the acaulescent Hellebores, this is actually a most attractive little species with a delicacy of form which is lost in some of the larger more robust ones. Its unscented wholly green flowers are usually only 2.5 to 3.5 cm in diameter, rarely a little more, and are overtopped by large leaf-like bracts which might result in it appearing a very leafy plant were it not for the fact that the basal leaves are normally poorly developed at flowering time. These basal leaves are strongly pedate with their central leaflets undivided, thus clearly distinguishing it from *H. multifidus*, another rather small green-flowered species, which has all the leaflets deeply divided. Both the basal leaves and bracts of *H. dumetorum* are furnished with rather fine serrations, a feature which helps to distinguish it from *H. viridis* which usually has very coarsely serrated leaves and generally larger flowers. In *H. dumetorum* the leaves are glabrous on the underside, or are sometimes furnished with very minute papillae in the very young stages, and they die away completely for the winter months, factors which distinguish this from the markedly evergreen *H. odorus* and the very hairy-leaved *H. cyclophyllus*, both of which in any case have much larger scented flowers. This combination of flower size and leaf characters make *H. dumetorum* a distinctive species within this complicated group of Balkan green- and purple-flowered species.

An interesting characteristic of *H. dumetorum* which I have noticed in both living material and dried specimens is that the roots are finer than those of other species, this being most noticeable at the point where they are attached to the rhizome, and there are rather a lot of them so that the rootstock consists of a mat of slender roots. Although this may be fairly obvious when fresh roots are observed in relation to those of another species, the difference in actual measurements is very slight, of the order of 0.5–1 mm thick in *H. dumetorum* and 1–2 mm in most other species. This is however scarcely a fundamental difference and is based on a fairly limited sample so I would not claim it to be highly significant and mention it only as a passing comment!

The epithet *dumetorum*, meaning of thickets or bushy places, is indicative of its preference for a partially shady habitat and it is often to be found in open Oak, Beech or Hornbeam woodland, growing with other early spring flowering plants such as *Anemone nemorosa* and *Corydalis bulbosa*. I remember vividly a site in southern Austria where these three species occurred together in a woodland glade making a charming scene long before the main flush of herbaceous vegetation appeared.

It is not a particularly widespread plant in the wild, occurring in the extreme southeast of Austria and adjacent northern Yugoslavia, in Slovenia and Croatia, eastwards into Hungary. In Hungary it is known in the hills and woods to the west of the Danube plain but appears to avoid the plain itself and reappears in

H. dumetorum

H. torquatus, a wild form collected in W. Yugoslavia near Bosanski Petrovak by Mr & Mrs H Crook

A *H. torquatus* x *H. orientalis* hybrid, similar to 'Ballard's Black'

An unspotted *H. orientalis* hybrid of a good clear colour

H. purpurascens

H. viridis x *H. orientalis* subsp.
guttatus hybrid from Elizabeth
Strangman

A curiously coloured 'guttatus' hybrid
by Helen Ballard, probably with *H.
torquatus* influence

Romania where it is recorded in the southwest, south and east of the country. It is cited in literature as also occurring in Czechoslovakia but I can find no real evidence for this and the authoritative Flora of that country indicates that it is not native but is occasionally cultivated, perhaps this also being the reason for its mention in other works. Thus, comparing the distribution of *H. dumetorum* with that of the other green-flowered species of the region, it occupies a more northerly area than *H. multifidus* and *H. cyclophyllus* and is more easterly-occurring than *H. viridis*, but does grow within the same general area as *H. odorus*.

H. dumetorum does not vary greatly in overall appearance but several forms have been named. These are however of no great interest to the gardener and are recorded only for the sake of completeness:

(a) **forma *incisus*** Schiffner. Apparently a form with deeply incised leaves rather than finely toothed.
(b) **forma *laciniatus*** Martinis. A form in which the leaflets have such coarse teeth as to be laciniate, the 'teeth' up to 1 cm long and themselves finely serrate at the margins.
(c) **forma *majoriflorus*** Borbas. A form with slightly larger flowers than usual.
(d) **forma *multisectus*** Schiffner. This is said to have most of the leaf segments subdivided and one wonders if indeed it is a form of *H. dumetorum* at all. However I have seen no herbarium material and cannot comment.
(e) **forma *pauciflorus*** Schiffner. A variant with 2–4 flowers per stem. In my experience, however, this is a fairly normal condition.

Cultivation

Although smaller and less coarse in its growth than other species there is nothing frail about *H. dumetorum* and it is a very tough, easily cultivated Hellebore, capable of withstanding more severe weather than, for example, *H. multifidus* and *H. cyclophyllus* which come from more southerly climes. The best specimens I have grown have been on a north-facing peat bed and in a partially shaded border with other woodlanders such as *Sanguinaria canadensis*, *Hepatica* and *Convallaria*. One pleasing combination, which came about by chance rather than design, occurred in the garden when that excellent ground cover plant, the blackish-leaved *Ophiopogon planiscapus* 'Nigrescens', surrounded a clump of *H. dumetorum* whose fresh spring green growth livened up and contrasted with the sombre background of the Ophiopogon so that the appearance of both plants was enhanced.

From the original plant which I brought from the wild many years ago I have raised seedlings which have come true with no apparent crossing, although there are plenty of other Hellebores in the garden. I very much doubt that it is incapable of crossing with other species and it may be that at the early season when it is flowering there are few pollinators about to effect cross-pollination. I know of no hybrids of *H. dumetorum* but if it were to cross with one of the very similar species such as *H. viridis* or *H. multifidus* it would in any case not be very easy to detect in the offspring that this had occurred. It has always been a fairly rare plant in cultivation so the chances of hybridisation are reduced for this reason alone. Robert Rolfe recalls seeing one exhibited at the RHS in 1982. It was apparently flushed pink towards the edges.

My own experience of *H. dumetorum* is that it is a very easily cultivated species, very hardy, and not very susceptible to damage by the leaf spot diseases which are such a problem with *H. multifidus* and *H. niger* in my garden.

H. dumetorum Waldst. & Kit. in Willd., Enum. Pl. Hort. Berol. 1: 592 (1809).

Type: 'Habitat in Hungaria' (?specimen in Prague, Czechoslovakia)

Synonyms

H. viridis var. *dumetorum* (Waldst. & Kit.) Sadl., Fl. Pestiensis 2: 64 (1826)

H. pallidus Host, Fl. Austr. 2: 90 (1831)

H. vaginatus Host, loc. cit.

H. viridis var. *pallidus* (Host) Schur, Enum. Pl. Trans: 27 (1886)

H. hunfalvyanus var. *dumetorum* (Waldst. & Kit.) Kanitz in Hunfalvys ung. Pflanzengeogr.

H. viridis subsp. *dumetorum* (Waldst. & Kit.) Hayek, Prodr. Fl. Penins. Balc. 1: 299 (1924)

Description

Glabrous (or nearly so) perennial herb, usually about 15–25(–30) cm in height at flowering time, with a tough rhizomatous rootstock and rather thin roots. Basal leaves 2–3, not overwintering, pedate with (7–)9–11(–13) segments, rather thin in texture, mid-green, the segments oblong-lanceolate or narrowly elliptic, about 6–10 cm long and 1–3 cm wide, tapered at the base, acute at the apex, glabrous or minutely papillose on the underside, the veins not markedly prominent beneath; margin regularly serrate; petioles 10–20 cm long, green. Cauline leaves (bract leaves) comparatively large and overtopping the flowers, pedately divided, the lower ones similar to the basal leaves, the upper ones much smaller and less divided, sometimes with only 3 segments, finely serrate. Inflorescences taller than the leaves at flowering time, usually with 2–4 flowers, on slender pedicels 1–2(–4) cm long. Flowers wholly green, unscented, nodding, cup-shaped, 2.5–3.5(–4) cm in diameter; perianth segments subequal or the two outer slightly narrower, not or scarcely overlapping, elliptic or obovate, rounded or obtuse at the apex, 1–2.2 cm long, 0.7–1.5 cm wide; nectaries 8–12, short-stalked, curved-funnel shaped with an oblique, uneven-toothed margin or sometimes bilobed at the mouth, green; stamens numerous, erect or suberect, anthers 1.5–2 mm long; carpels 2–5, fused at the base; styles exceeding the stamens, straight or slightly curved outwards. Follicles about 1.5–1.8 cm long at maturity; seeds ellipsoid, about 4 mm long with a distinct ridge on one side.

Flowering time March–May (in the wild).

Habitat Mountain woods and thickets.

Distribution S. Austria, N. Yugoslavia, W. Hungary, S.W., S. & E. Romania.

12 *Helleborus viridis*

The Green Hellebore is the most widespread of the green-flowered species, occurring over the whole of western Europe from Spain eastwards to Germany and Austria and from Britain and Belgium in the north, as far south as Switzerland and northern Italy. For the greater part of this range it is somewhat small-flowered and has rather weakly pedate leaves with very coarsely jagged margins. The bracts are quite large and also coarsely toothed and the flowers are carried on long-stemmed branches, so with these various features it is generally not at all difficult to recognise. The only other small-flowered Hellebore, *H. dumetorum*, has very strongly pedate leaves looking quite different from those of *H. viridis*, and the flowers are even smaller. In British plants the upper surface of the leaves of *H. viridis* tend to have a dark shiny appearance whereas the foliage of *H. dumetorum* is a paler dull green above. However I do not know if this is a characteristic of *H. viridis* over its whole range. Both species are winter-deciduous which serves to distinguish them from *H. odorus* whose leaves remain green through the winter until after flowering time, and in addition this species has noticeably larger flowers than those of *H. viridis* and *H. dumetorum* which are unscented. In Italy and Yugoslavia the related species is the deciduous *H. multifidus* in which all the leaflets are divided into several segments, although in the north of its range the plants have far fewer divisions than those in the south. With regard to hairiness, or lack of it, it can be said that in general *H. viridis* and *H. dumetorum* have glabrous leaves, while those of *H. odorus* and *H. multifidus* have varying degrees of pubescence on the underside. The only other European green-flowered species of this group is *H. cyclophyllus* from the southern Balkans but this need not enter into the discussion about *H. viridis* since it has large flowers in which the carpels are free from each other right to the base; in the other four species mentioned they are fused together for a short distance at the base.

Unfortunately, although *H. viridis* is clearly distinguishable from these other species over much of its area of distribution, the position becomes somewhat clouded in the south and east of its range, notably in northern Italy and Austria where the flowers are larger and the leaves more strongly pedate and slightly hairy on the underside. The species was described by Linnaeus who gave the origin as 'Viennensibus, Euganeis', that is, Austria and northern Italy, and his type specimen represents one of these larger-flowered plants. The more westerly and northerly occurring variant was described by Reuter in 1868 as *H. occidentalis*, with the localities 'Gallia occidentali, Pyrenaeis, Hispania boreali'. It appears, however, that there are no consistent differences between the two and in some areas there is a gradation from one to the other so in view of this *H. viridis* and *H. occidentalis* have been merged by most authors under the oldest name *H. viridis*. The western variant was not ignored however, for Schiffner (1889) maintained it as subsp. *occidentalis* and this view has been followed by most other authors, including Merxmüller and Podlech (1961) whose important studies formed the basis for the treatment of *Helleborus* in *Flora Europaea* (1964). The distinguishing features given by *Flora Europaea* are as follows:

subsp. *viridis*. Leaves pubescent beneath; segments finely serrate. Perianth segments broadly ovate. C. Europe and Maritime Alps.

subsp. *occidentalis*. Leaves glabrous beneath; segments coarsely serrate. Perianth segments narrower. W. Europe.

Plants from northern Italy pose certain problems over identification and a detailed field study might prove valuable in resolving the matter. It seems to me that *H. viridis* subsp. *viridis* and *H. multifidus* subsp. *bocconei*, and possibly also *H. multifidus* subsp. *istriacus*, are in close proximity in this area and a possible answer to the problem of classification is that hybridisation is taking place, resulting in intermediate populations in which the species characteristics are obscured. One collection which I have from the northern Apennines, for example, has rather large scented flowers, more like those of *H. multifidus* subsp. *bocconei*, but the pedate leaves have rather few divisions, quite unlike those of the latter and more like those of *H. viridis*.

H. viridis is a plant of deciduous woodlands and is almost always to be found on calcareous soils, often in heavy clay. In Britain it is not a common plant but is widespread on the chalk and limestone formations and may occur in considerable quantities in limited areas. I have also seen it growing in woods off the chalk hills but alongside streams which originate at the foot of the Downs, presumably carrying alkaline water. It does not vary a great deal in appearance wherever I have seen it in England, although in one population in Surrey I did find a plant with purple blotches on the inside, one at the base of each of the perianth segments; this variant has been described as forma *maculatus* by C.E. Salmon, author of the *Flora of Surrey* (1931).

H. viridis has a long history in cultivation, mainly as a medicinal plant in the early days. It was certainly known to John Gerard (1597) who described its uses and remarked that it was grown in London gardens (see page 16).

Cultivation
As a garden plant *H. viridis* is not one of the most spectacular, nevertheless it has a quiet charm which appeals to those who prefer the more subtle subdued colours of the species Hellebores. It is not difficult to cultivate and seems to do best when planted in a semi-shaded position in heavy soil which will not dry out too much in the summer.

H. viridis Linn., Sp. Pl.: 558 (1753).
Type: 'Habitat in montibus Viennensibus [Austria], Euganeis [Italy]' (specimen in Linnean Society Herbarium, London).

Description (of the species as a whole)
Glabrous or sparsely pubescent perennial herb, usually about 20–40 cm in height at flowering time, with a tough rhizomatous rootstock and fairly thick roots. Basal leaves usually 2, not overwintering, weakly pedate or more distinctly pedate with 7–13 segments, rather thin in texture, often deep green and glossy above, the

segments oblong-lanceolate or narrowly elliptic, about 6–10 cm long and 1–3 cm wide, tapered at the base, acute or shortly acuminate at the apex, glabrous or sparsely hairy on the underside, the veins slender but prominent beneath; margin irregularly and coarsely dentate-serrate or more finely serrate; petioles 10–20 cm long, green. Bracts large and overtopping the flowers, weakly pedate to more or less palmate, coarsely serrate. Inflorescences equalling or exceeding the newly emerging leaves at flowering time, usually with 2–4 flowers on long branches, carried on slender pedicels 1–4 cm long. Flowers wholly green, occasionally with a purple blotch at the base of each perianth segment, unscented, nodding, saucer-shaped or flattish, (3–)3.5–5 cm in diameter; perianth segments subequal, overlapping, broadly elliptic or ovate, rounded or obtuse at the apex, 1.3–2.4 cm long, 0.7–1.6 cm wide; nectaries 9–12, short-stalked, funnel-shaped and curved with an oblique uneven-toothed margin, green; stamens numerous, erect or suberect; anthers 1.5–2 mm long; carpels (2)3–4, fused or slightly curved outwards. Follicles about 1.5–1.8 cm long at maturity; seeds ellipsoid, about 4 mm long with a small ridge on one side.

Two subspecies are recognised:

(a) subsp. *viridis*

Synonyms
Helleboraster viridis (L.) Moench, Method. Pl. Hort. Bot. Marburg.: 236 (1794)
Helleborus viridis var. *jacquinianus* A. Braun in Ind. Sem. Hort. Berol., appendix: 14 (1861).
H. brevicaulis Fourr. in Nyman, Consp.: 17 (1878).
H. hunfalvyanus Kan. var. *viridis* (L.) Kanitz in Hunfalvys Ungar. Pflanzengeog.

Description
Leaves distinctly pedate, sparsely pubescent beneath, segments serrate. Flowers 4–5 cm diameter.

Flowering time March–April in the wild, February–March in cultivation.

Habitat Deciduous woods and in scrub, usually on calcareous formations, up to 1100 metres.

Distribution SE France, Switzerland, N. Italy, S. Germany, Austria.

(b) subsp. *occidentalis* (Reut.) Schiffner in Bot. Jahrb. 11: 118 (1889).
Type: 'Gallia occidentali, Pyrenaeis, Hispania boreali'.

Synonyms
H. occidentalis Reuter, Cat. Grain. Genéve, rec. 1868; and in Bull. Soc. Bot. France 16: Revue Bibl.: 53 (1869).
H. viridis var. *smithianus* A. Braun in Ind. Sem. Hort. Berol. appendix: 14 (1861)

H. viridis var. *smithianus* forma *maculatus* Salmon in Flora of Surrey: 103 (1931).

Description
Leaves weakly pedate, glabrous beneath, segments very coarsely dentate-serrate. Flowers (3–)3.5–4 cm diameter.

Flowering time March–April in the wild, February–March in cultivation.

Habitat Moist calcareous deciduous woodland, coppices or scrub, to 1700 metres.

Distribution Britain (especially south and west, probably native as far north as Westmorland and Yorkshire); Belgium, France, Spain, W. Germany ?Switzerland, ?Austria.

H. viridis has been introduced, and is sometimes naturalised, in several other countries, probably as a result of its former use for medicinal purposes.

13 *Helleborus odorus*

Of the green-flowered species *H. odorus* is, as a garden plant, probably one of the best, since it has large scented flowers and is fairly hardy. It is preferable to *H. viridis* and *H. dumetorum* on account of its superior flower size and is, I find, better than *H. multifidus* and *H. cyclophyllus* in terms of hardiness, although it can be damaged in severe winters.

Its main characteristic features are, as with most of these Balkan species, to be found in the leaves, which in the case of *H. odorus* are pedately divided with the central leaflet entire and the lateral ones subdivided, usually into rather few broad segments. The underside is fairly densely covered with long hairs so that as the young leaves push through the ground they are silvery-hairy. The foliage is very tough and remains green through the winter, at least until flowering time when the new leaves emerge, so in this feature it differs from the other related green-flowered species. In my experience, all others are deciduous and lose their leaves in autumn. Sometimes, however, in mild winters, those of *H. cyclophyllus* do overwinter, and I have seen herbarium specimens which indicate that in the wild the old leaves of *H. multifidus* subsp. *multifidus* and subsp. *bocconei* may sometimes remain green until flowering time.

The large green flowers of *H. odorus* are between 5 cm and 7 cm in diameter and have a strong fragrance somewhat reminiscent of *Ribes sanguineum*, a scent which is also to be found in *H. multifidus* and *H. cyclophyllus*. Since the flower size alone is sufficient to distinguish *H. odorus* from *H. dumetorum*, and its leaf characters are distinct from those of *H. multifidus* and *H. viridis*, it is really only necessary to compare it critically with *H. cyclophyllus*. The feature which has traditionally been used to separate them, certainly since the time of Schiffner, is whether the carpels are fused together at the base or are completely free from each other and are carried separately upon the cone-shaped receptacle. In *H. cyclophyllus* (and the *H. orientalis* complex) they are stated to be free while in all the other Balkan species they are joined together. It is necessary to point out that they are fused for only a few millimetres so that it is best to study a number of flowers of different species (for example *H. orientalis* and *H. viridis*) to get an 'eye in' for this particular feature before applying it critically to specimens which are suspected to be *H. odorus* or *H. cyclophyllus*. In the 1960s and 1970s I travelled widely in Yugoslavia, Greece and Bulgaria and looked fairly carefully at this character in *H. cyclophyllus* and decided that it was variable in parts of southern Yugoslavia and Bulgaria and that in some populations both types could be found. Greek plants however had free carpels, and inspection of a wider range of herbarium specimens appears to support the general observation that the southernmost plants are 'good' *H. cyclophyllus*, with no tendency for their carpels to be joined. It seems best to me if both *H. odorus* and *H. cyclophyllus* are maintained as distinct species, *H. odorus* being the more northerly-occurring plant with overwintering leaves and carpels joined at the base, while *H. cyclophyllus* refers to plants with winter-deciduous leaves and free carpels and having a southern distribution in Albania, southern Yugoslavia, Bulgaria and Greece. *H. odorus* is found widely across inland Yugoslavia from Slavonia and Croatia south to Montenegro and Macedonia and the most likely explanation is that there is hybridisation with *H. cyclophyllus* in the south of this range, thus obscuring the distinguishing characteristics in this area. Although not a hard and fast rule, one might add that there is a general tendency for the flowers of *H. odorus* to be of a darker richer green than those of *H. cyclophyllus*, in which they are often of a pale yellow-green shade.

These two species are undeniably very similar and at least one modern Flora of the region, *Flora na Bulgariya* (1966), has united them under the oldest name of *H. odorus*.

Such a variable plant as *H. odorus* has, not surprisingly, attracted attention from those who like to provide names for every minor variant, but even within some of these named forms there is still quite a wide range of variability. The following list gives some indication of this variation and the extent to which the species has been fragmented by certain botanists.

(a) **forma *angustifolius*** Beck: Leaflets up to 2 cm wide.
(b) **forma *javorkae*** Horvat: Flowers with pointed tepals.
(c) **forma *laceratus*** K. Maly: Leaflets with very deeply incised margins.
(d) **forma *latifolius*** Beck: Particularly wide leaflets 3–6 cm broad.
(e) **forma *mecsekensis*** Horvat: Leaves becoming glabrous beneath as they age.
(f) **forma *multisectus*** Martinis: Leaf segments somewhat subdivided (perhaps through hybridisation with *H. multifidus* since both occur in W. Yugoslavia).
(g) **forma *odorus***: The typical form with leaflets 2–3 cm wide, the central one undivided.
(h) **forma *parviflorus*** Priszter: Flowers slightly smaller than usual.
(i) **forma *purpureiformis*** Horvat: Flowers purplish outside (perhaps caused by hybridisation with *H. purpurascens* or *H. atrorubens* in areas where the populations are closest geographically).

Reference should also be made here to Host's *H. laxus* since, in *Flora*

Europaea, Merxmüller and Podlech treated this as a subspecies of *H. odorus*, giving the distribution as N.W. Yugoslavia and N. Italy. Z. Martinis, however, in *Analitička Flora Jugoslavije* (1973), regarded it a variant of *H. multifidus* and this seems more appropriate. Schiffner's *H. odorus* var. *istriacus* is also more akin to *H. multifidus* than it is to *H. odorus* and can be considered as another variant of that very variable species.

Host's *H. graveolens*, described in 1831 from N. Yugoslavia is, judging from its original description, best treated as a variant of *H. odorus*. Schiffner (1889) interpreted it as an *odorus* × *atrorubens* hybrid, while Ulbrich (1938) regarded it as a distinct species, noting that its flowers were unpleasantly scented and had green perianth segments tinged violet at the edges. Host, however, had made no mention of any violet coloration, or of flower scent, and it was in fact the leaves which were said to be 'graveolentia'. The leaf shape was described as pedate with the median leaflet entire, and the underside was noted as being pubescent, both features of *H. odorus*.

Cultivation

H. odorus is an easily cultivated species for a semi-shaded position in humus-rich soil and is one of the best of the green-flowered species for garden display. It shows up particularly well when placed in a spot in dappled sunlight with a dark background to accentuate the bright green flowers. It is a fairly hardy species but is susceptible to black spot diseases and I find that a regular fungicidal spray in spring is necessary to prevent the flowers being ruined. Undoubtedly *H. odorus* is one of the species which has been used in the breeding of the yellowish strains of 'orientalis hybrids' and is responsible for their rather pleasing stocky habit with the flowers facing outwards rather than drooping as in most of the purple coloured hybrids.

H. odorus Waldst. & Kit. in Willd., Enum. Pl. Hort. Berol. 1: 592 (1809).
Type: "Habitat in Hungaria".

Synonyms

H. graveolens Host, Fl. Austriaca 2: 89 (1831)

H. viridis var. *odorus* (Waldst. & Kit.) Kittel, Taschenbuch Fl. Deutschl. ed. 2: 781 (1844).

H. decorus Le Bele, Monogr. di Hell. ex C. Koch in Allg. Berl. Gartenz.: 162 (1858).

H. hunfalvyanus var. *odorus* (Waldst. & Kit.) Kanitz in Schulzer v. Mügganb., Kanitz & Knapp, Pflanzen. Slavon.: 138 (1866).

Description

Perennial herb, often only 10–20 cm in height at flowering time, but elongating up to 30 cm later on; rhizome tough with stout roots. Basal leaves overwintering, thick and leathery, pedate with the central leaflet usually undivided, the lateral ones each deeply divided into 3–5 lobes, normally giving a total of 7–11

H. viridis subsp. *occidentalis*

H. 'Paul Mathew' raised by Brian Mathew
by selection from *H. orientalis*
subsp. *guttatus* seedlings

H. 'Margaret Mathew' a large-flowered
H. orientalis hybrid with
finely speckled perianth segments

H. orientalis subsp. *guttatus*, a good large-flowered selection

H. 'Hidcote Double'. A double *H. orientalis*
hybrid found by Graham Thomas
growing at Hidcote Manor, Gloucestershire

A double *H. orientalis* hybrid raised in Germany

H. multifidus subsp. *hercegovinus*

segments; leaflets and segments elliptic or oblanceolate, up to 20 cm long and up to 6.5 cm wide, densely hairy on the underside, usually over the whole under-surface but sometimes only on the stout prominent veins; margin coarsely serrate; petioles 13–28 cm long, green. Bracts rather small, often shorter than or equalling the flowers but occasionally overlapping them, divided into 3–5 serrate segments. Inflorescences fairly short when the first flowers open, usually carrying 3–5 flowers, rarely unbranched with only one flower and occasionally, in more vigorous specimens, widely branched with up to 7 flowers. Flowers usually 5–6(–7) cm diameter (later flowers on a branch are often smaller), scented, facing outwards rather than nodding, saucer-shaped, green, carried on short stout pedicels up to 1 cm long at first but elongating in the fruiting stage; perianth segments equal or subequal and overlapping, broadly ovate, broadly elliptical or suborbicular, obtuse or rounded, usually 2.5–3.5 cm long, 2–2.6 cm wide; nectaries distinctly stalked, widely funnel-shaped, curved with a slightly oblique or truncate mouth, scarcely toothed at the margin, green; stamens numerous, erect or suberect, anthers about 2 mm long; carpels 3–5(–6), fused together for 2–3 mm at the base; styles usually exceeding the stamens, straight or slightly curved. Follicles 1.5–2 cm long at maturity (excluding the style), narrowed abruptly at the base; seeds about 5 mm long, dark brown with a distinct ridge on one side.

Flowering time February–April in the wild, January–March in cultivation.

Habitat Wood margins often in *Quercus* (Oak) or *Fagus* (Beech) and in thickets, sometimes in grassland, usually on calcareous formations, sea level to 1700 metres.

Distribution Yugoslavia (except extreme W. and extreme S.), S. Hungary, S. Romania, doubtfully extending into N. Bulgaria and N. Italy.

14 *Helleborus multifidus*

The specific name of this green-flowered species refers to the leaves, the leaflets of which are divided to varying degrees into narrow segments. In one of its extreme forms, known as subsp. *hercegovinus*, which is to be found in southern Hercegovina, especially the Dubrovnik and Kotor regions of the Adriatic coast of Yugoslavia, it is perhaps the most interesting of all the Hellebores for foliage effect with a great many narrow divisions per leaf. Indeed it is so striking that it might well be worth trying to hybridise this subspecies with the coloured *H. orientalis* cultivars in an attempt to enhance the rather coarse unattractive foliage of the latter.

In the wild *H. multifidus* is a plant of sparse deciduous woods and open grassy scrubland on limestone hills and mountains where it becomes rather hot and dry in the summer months. The flowers slightly precede the leaves but by the late flowering period, the young foliage, which is often bronze-tinged and hairy at first, is beginning to emerge. The pendent yellowish-green flowers are of medium size, varying from 3.5–6 cm in diameter and are somewhat conical in shape. The southern Italian and Sicilian variant, subsp. *bocconei*, is on the whole the largest flowered, sometimes up to 6 cm in diameter, whereas Yugoslavian forms may be as little as 3.5 cm, although there is a fair amount of overlap in size. All the *H. multifidus* variants are scented with a fragrance similar to that of *H. odorus* (Ribes-like), but usually not as strong.

H. multifidus is, as with most species, variable, and in this particular case the variability is exceptional, leading to taxonomic confusion and duplication of names. The locality given by Roberto de Visiani in 1829 for the original specimen is rather vague, merely the Dalmatian mountains. His herbarium material, of which there is one sheet at Kew, shows a plant with fairly well-divided leaves but with not nearly as many segments as the plants from southern Hercegovina mentioned above. Visiani's plant is, it seems, fairly typical of those to be found in the central coastal mountains of Yugoslavia, for example in the vicinity of Split, and this variant must be regarded as subsp. *multifidus*. Northwards along the coast to the peninsula of Istria, inland into the limestone karst country of northwestern Yugoslavia and westwards into northeastern Italy the foliage is less divided and the individual segments of the leaflets are wider. This variant has been described as subsp. *istriacus* (Waldst. & Kit.) Merxm. & Podlech and is an extremely common plant throughout NW Yugoslavia. Although there is an overlap in characters between this and subsp. *multifidus* it is convenient to continue to recognise these variants rather than to 'lump' them into one. Since there is a geographical correlation with the leaf characters it is appropriate to give them subspecific status.

Host's *H. laxus*, also from northern Yugoslavia, would appear to be based on a variant with rather few leaf divisions and it is probably best to merge this with *H. multifidus* subsp. *istriacus*. It has in the past been linked with *H. odorus* and with *H. viridis* but recently Z. Martinis (1973), in his study of the Yugoslavian Hellebores, allied it to *H. multifidus*, and I agree that this is the most closely related species. To me, the most likely explanation of this variation is that in this region the populations of *H. multifidus* with less finely divided leaves are the result of introgression by *H. odorus* which occurs in northern Yugoslavia. This has strongly pedate leaves with a few broad segments, the median one of which is undivided, and presumably its influence on *H. multifidus* would be to depress the number of leaf divisions.

Southwards along the Adriatic coastal mountains of Yugoslavia to the Albanian border occurs the form mentioned above which has the most finely divided leaves of any Hellebore, with sixty or more narrow segments, each only 3–6 mm wide. This was described as *H. hercegovinus* by Z. Martinis (1973) from specimens gathered in April 1913 by K. Maly on Mt. Orjen near Kotor. For much of the time since Maly collected it this has been regarded as the true *H. multifidus* and plants introduced to cultivation by myself in 1966, and by others, have been grown under that name in gardens. It does however seem to be rather distinct from the more northern populations and is restricted to a definite region. I agree with Martinis that it should be given some recognition, although at the rank of subspecies to indicate its close affinity with *H. multifidus*. It is quite likely that this variant occurs also in the adjacent parts of Albania although I have seen no specimens to authenticate this. In its natural habitat, *H. multifidus* subsp.

hercegovinus grows in association with deciduous oaks, *Arum nigrum*, *Crocus tommasinianus*, *C. dalmaticus*, *C. biflorus* ssp. *weldenii*, *Fritillaria gracilis* and *Galanthus reginae-olgae* var. *vernalis*. It is certainly one of the most distinct of the green-flowered Hellebores and well worth cultivating.

In central and southern Italy and Sicily the divided-leaved Hellebores of this group have been described as *H. bocconei* Tenore and *H. siculus* Schiffner respectively. The former was said to differ from *H. multifidus* on account of the segments of its leaves being less deeply divided, while the latter was distinguished by having rather small leaves, glabrous beneath. Flower size has also been used as a distinguishing feature between the Italian and Yugoslavian plants but this does not appear to be very reliable, although it can be said that on the whole the Italian variants have larger flowers (4.5–6 cm in diameter) than the Yugoslavian ones in which they are 3.5–5.5 cm in diameter. Thus there is a 4.5–5.5 cm overlap zone which makes this character of rather low diagnostic value, but nevertheless it is a trend which should be noted. The taxonomic treatments of this Italian material are varied. Schiffner (1889) regarded *H. bocconei* as a variety of *H. multifidus* but at the same time described *H. siculus* as a separate species. Ulbrich (1938), on the other hand, kept *H. bocconei* separate from *H. multifidus* as a distinct species, into which he 'sank' *H. siculus*, while Merxmüller and Podlech (1961) retained *H. bocconei* and recognised *siculus* as a subspecies of it. In view of the geographical separation, coupled with the rather slight morphological differences between *H. multifidus* and *H. bocconei* it would seem appropriate to recognise the latter as a subspecies of *H. multifidus*, but I can see little reason for keeping the Sicilian representatives (*H. siculus*) separate from subsp. *bocconei* since there is much variation in the degree of hairiness and overall size of leaf.

Cultivation

Helleborus multifidus is, as mentioned above, an attractive foliage plant, especially in its subsp. *hercegovinus*, and is worth growing for this reason alone. The green flowers are usually not quite as large as those of *H. odorus* and *H. cyclophyllus* so as a flowering plant it is certainly not so interesting. I find that it requires a sheltered position with slightly more sun and better drainage than most Hellebores and it almost certainly does better on alkaline soils. It suffers badly in damp cold winters which is hardly surprising when one considers its natural habitat and rather southerly distribution. It also seems to be rather susceptible to the leaf spot diseases (see page 159) but this is undoubtedly partly due to the fact that the plants I have are not growing vigorously anyway. Plants cultivated in the order beds at Kew indicate that it will tolerate full sun, although they do not flower very freely. Subsp. *bocconei* is a slightly better garden plant, some forms rivalling *H. odorus* in flower size, and in general it appears to be more vigorous, at least in Britain, than subsp. *multifidus* or subsp. *hercegovinus*. However, in severe winters the young flowering shoots may be damaged by frosts, particularly if an early-flowering form is being grown. The variation in flowering time is considerable and E.B. Anderson (1957) noted that it could be in flower before Christmas; on the whole however, it is an early spring flowering plant, in February or March.

H. multifidus Visiani, Pl. Rar. Dalm. in Bot. Zeit. 1: 18 (1829).
Type: Yugoslavia, 'In tota montana Dalmatiae', *Visiani* (specimen at Kew).

(a) subsp. *multifidus*

Synonyms
H. angustifolius Host, Fl. Aust. 2: 190 (1831)
H. viridis var. *multifidus* (Vis.) Vis., Fl. Dalm. 3: 88 (1850)
H. hunfalvyanus var. *multifidus* (Vis.) Kanitz in Aschers. & Kanitz, Catal. Serb.
  Bosn. Herzeg. 73, no. 2027 (1877)
H. odorus subsp. *multifidus* (Vis.) Hayek in Feddes Repert. Beih. 30(1): 299
  (1924)

Description (of subsp. *multifidus*)
Perennial herb, usually about 20–30 cm in height at flowering time, with a tough
rhizomatous rootstock and stout roots. Basal leaves usually not overwintering,
green, leathery in texture when mature, pedate (although this may be obscured by
the many narrow divisions) with all the leaflets divided to more than half way
resulting in about 20–45 segments; segments linear-lanceolate, up to 13 cm long
and 1–1.5 cm wide, usually hairy on the underside, especially on the stout
prominent veins, but sometimes glabrous; margins coarsely serrate at maturity;
petioles up to 30 cm long, green or purplish-brown at the base. Bracts divided
deeply into 2–8 narrow segments, coarsely serrate. Inflorescence usually taller
than the developing leaves, branched and carrying 3–8 flowers. Flowers 3.5–
4.5 cm diameter, scented, nodding, rather conical cup-shaped, green, carried on
stout pedicels up to 1.5 cm long at first, elongating in the fruiting stage; perianth
segments equal or subequal, elliptic or ovate-elliptic, not or just slightly
overlapping, obtuse, usually 2–2.5 cm long, 1.1–1.8 cm wide; nectaries about 10,
distinctly stalked, funnel-shaped, curved, oblique at the mouth and slightly waved
or toothed on the margin, green. Stamens numerous, erect or suberect, anthers
1.5–2.5 mm long; carpels 3–4, fused together at the base, styles equalling or
slightly exceeding the stamens, straight or slightly curved. Follicles about 2 cm
long at maturity (excluding the style), narrowed abruptly at the base; seeds about
4–5 mm long, dark or reddish-brown with a distinct ridge on one side.

Flowering period April–May in the wild, January–April in cultivation.

Habitat Scrub, light woodland and grassy slopes, up to 1500 metres.

Distribution Yugoslavia, in the central region of the Adriatic coastal mountains.

(b) subsp. *hercegovinus* (Martinis) B. Mathew

Type: Yugoslavia, Hercegovina, Mt. Orjen, 6 April 1913, *K. Maly* (specimens in Sarajevo & Kew)

Synonym

H. hercegovinus Martinis in Suppl. Fl. Anal. Jugosl. 1: 13 (1973).

Description

Similar in most details to subsp. *multifidus* but basal leaves green or brownish when young, dissected into 45–70 linear or narrowly linear-lanceolate segments mostly less than 6 mm wide, hairy on the underside. Flowers 4–5 cm in diameter.

Flowering period March–April in the wild, February–March in cultivation.

Habitat Rocky hillsides in grassy places or in oak scrub or light woodland, up to 1600 m.

Distribution Yugoslavia, Hercegovina, in the southern Adriatic coastal mountains, possibly also adjacent Albania.

(c) subsp. *istriacus* (Schiffner) Merxmüller & Podlech in Feddes Repert. Sp. Nov. 64: 5 (1961).

Type: Yugoslavia, Istria, near Rijeka, *Schulz, Reuss. fil., Roth.*

Synonyms

H. laxus Host, Fl. Aust. 2: 89 (1831)

H. viridis var. *laxus* (Host) Kittel, Taschenbuch Fl. Deutsch. ed. 2: 781 (1844)

H. odorus var. *istriacus* Schiffner in Engl. Bot. Jahrb. 11: 114 (1889)

H. istriacus (Schiffner) Borbas in Öst. Bot. Zeit. 42: 219 (1892)

H. odorus subsp. *laxus* (Host) Merxmüller & Podlech in Feddes Repert. Sp. Nov. 64: 5 (1961)

H. multifidus forma *istriacus* (Schiffner) Martinis in Suppl. Fl. Anal. Jugosl. 1: 15 (1973).

H. multifidus subsp. *laxus* (Host) Martinis in Suppl. Fl. Anal. Jugosl. 1: 15 (1973)

Description

Similar in most details to subsp. *multifidus* but basal leaves with fewer divisions, and more clearly pedate, with 10–14 segments, the main ones 2–3.5 cm wide; segments hairy on the undersides; margins rather more finely serrate. Flowers 4–5.5 cm diameter.

Flowering period February–April in the wild and in cultivation.

Habitat In grassy scrub and light woodland, 500–1500 metres.

Distribution N.W. Yugoslavia, N.E. Italy.

(d) subsp. *bocconei* (Tenore) B. Mathew
Type: Italy, 'in nemoribus montium Lucaniae et Calabriae'

Synonyms
H. bocconei Tenore, Prodr. Fl. Nap. App. 4: 26 (1823).
H. intermedius Guss., Pl. Rar. Ion. et Adriat.: 224, t. 41 (1826)
H. viridis var. *bocconei* (Tenore) Baker in Gard. Chron. N.S. 7: 464 (1877)
H. multifidus var. *bocconei* (Tenore) Schiffner in Engl. Bot. Jahrb. 11: 115 (1889)
H. siculus Schiffner in Engl. Bot. Jahrb. 11: 116 (1889)

Description
Similar in most details to subsp. *multifidus* but leaflets divided to about half way or less, glabrous or slightly hairy on the undersides; margins grossly toothed; bracts large and very coarsely toothed. Flowers 4.5–6 cm diameter.

Flowering period March–April in the wild, (November–)January–March in cultivation.

Habitat Light woodland or scrub, 500–1800 metres.

Distribution Central & S. Italy, Sicily.

SECTION SIX

Dicarpon

15 *Helleborus thibetanus*

Although I have not had the good fortune to see *H. thibetanus* in its living state it is clear from the herbarium material available that it is a most attractive species and certainly well worth introducing to gardens for its undoubted aesthetic appeal as well as for botanical interest.

The initial impression is of a perfectly orthodox Hellebore with nothing outstandingly different about it, much like *H. viridis* in stature and overall appearance since it has coarsely serrate basal leaves, which are pedately divided, and medium sized flowers, although these are of a quite different colour. Indeed, although it was first described as a species by Franchet in 1885, it was reduced to the status of a variety of *H. viridis* in 1904 by Finet & Gagnepain. This view was however not upheld by Dr Ulbrich in his monograph of the genus in 1938, or by Wang Wen-tsai in the more recent *Flora of the People's Republic of China* (1979). Ulbrich, in fact, went much further than restoring it to specific rank and placed it in a separate section from *H. viridis*. The section name Dicarpon relates to the fact that the flowers of *H. thibetanus* normally possess only two carpels although I have seen a specimen with three and the *Flora of China* also indicates that this is an occasional possibility. Within this section Ulbrich included *H. chinensis*, which was described by Maximowicz in 1890, making the observation that he had not seen any material and that it was a little-known species. The original description of *H. chinensis* does differ slightly from that of *H. thibetanus* but allowing for a certain amount of natural variation it is clear that only one species is involved in China, and the *Flora of China* therefore takes the view that *H. chinensis* is a synonym of *H. thibetanus*. One of the features given by Maximowicz for *H. chinensis*, namely the lack of any basal leaves, is almost certainly just a misinterpretation based on herbarium material. The inflorescences are sometimes well developed before the basal leaves begin to unfold and, viewed at an early stage, one might conceivably assume that this species possesses no basal leaves at all.

On the question of relationships there is no doubt that this Chinese Hellebore is morphologically close to the acaulescent species and bears little resemblance to the caulescent ones (*H. foetidus*, *H. lividus* and *H. argutifolius*) which possess woody leafy stems and lack any basal leaves. Conversely, however, palynological studies by Nowicke & Skvarla (1983) show that pollen grains of *H. thibetanus* have a *finely* reticulate tectum similar to that of the caulescent species, and they go so far as to suggest that 'it may be misplaced in the acaulescent group'; the species of the latter group (i.e. section *Helleborastrum*) have pollen grains with a *coarsely* reticulate tectum. Given this information the most realistic approach to the classification is to regard *H. thibetanus* (*H. chinensis*) as a distinct species and to maintain for it the separate section *Dicarpon* in which Ulbrich placed it in 1938.

H. thibetanus has branching inflorescences carrying several flowers, each about 4–6 cm in diameter with rather pointed perianth segments. From the herbarium material seen it appears that the colour is pink, delicately veined darker, although the notes on one specimen I have seen suggest that it may also be red-flowered. Since there is hardly any leaf development at flowering time, which is between early March and early April, a well-flowered clump must be a very showy sight indeed, for each stem may bear up to seven flowers all open at one time. When the basal leaves do expand they are strictly pedate with up to ten segments which are very coarsely jagged-toothed at the margins and apparently rather thin in texture.

The original specimen of *H. thibetanus* was collected at Moupin in Sichuan (Szechuan) province, while the type of material of *H. chinensis* came from Gansu (Kansu). It has also been found in Shaanxi (Shensi) province so it appears that, although these three provinces are adjacent to each other, this is not a very restricted plant in the wild. It is somewhat surprising that it has not yet found its way into cultivation, particularly when one considers that such thorough collectors as William Purdom and Joseph Rock saw it and prepared herbarium material. Purdom did gather it in the fruiting stage and sent a specimen to Messrs Veitch, which is now at Kew, so he would almost certainly have sent seeds also. However I can find no record of the species ever having been in cultivation so presumably his introductions did not survive, if indeed the seeds germinated at all. In 1980 I did obtain direct from China some seeds which were only six months old when sown but, sadly, these made no attempt to germinate and as far as I know *H. thibetanus* remains a temptation from afar.

Cultivation

The Chinese Hellebore should not be a difficult plant to cultivate once introduced since its natural habitat appears to be in rather shady moist woods, described as rain forest in one set of field notes. Ulbrich suggests that it would not be suitable for growing in the open garden but since it occurs over an altitude range of 1100–3700 metres it is likely to be hardy enough to survive in European gardens. Given the opportunity of growing it, I would suggest a leafmould-rich soil in the partial shade from deciduous shrubs.

H. thibetanus Franchet in Nouv. Arch. Mus. Paris ser. 2, 8: 190 (1885).

Type: China, Sichuan (Szechuan) Province, 'Moupine', March 1869, *David* (specimen in Paris herbarium).

Synonyms

H. chinensis Maximowicz in Acta Hort. Petrop. 11: 27 (1890)
H. viridis var. *thibetanus* (Franch.) Finet & Gagn. in Bull. Soc. Bot. France, Sér 4, 4: 397 (1904)

H. multifidus subsp. *bocconei*

Helleborus seed pods (follicles): (A) *H. argutifolius*; (B) *H. foetidus*; (C) *H. vesicarius*; (D) *H. orientalis* showing the free, stalked follicles; (E) *H. niger*

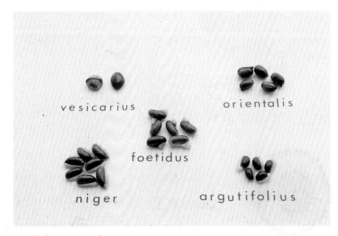

Helleborus seeds

Medicinal 'Black Hellebore' root

Description

Glabrous perennial herb 30–50 cm in height with a tough rhizomatous rootstock. Leaves 1 (rarely 2?) per shoot, not overwintering, poorly developed at flowering time, pedate with (7–)8–10 segments, only the lateral leaflets divided; leaflets and their lobes elliptic–oblanceolate, up to 15 cm long, 2–4.5 cm wide, cuneate at the base, acute at the apex; margin coarsely and sharply serrate, the teeth up to 6 mm long; petioles 10–20 cm long. Inflorescences consisting of loosely branched cymes of 2–8 flowers on stout peduncles 10–35 cm in height; bracts with 3–5 divisions, of similar shape to the basal leaves, and with the same coarse toothing, but smaller, usually 3.5–9 cm long. Flowers pale pink (?or red) with conspicuous veining, flattish, (3–)4–6(–6.5) cm in diameter; sepals rather thin in texture, equal, ovate–elliptic, (1.1–)1.6–2.3(–3.3) cm long, (0.5–)1–1.6(–2) cm wide, usually acute, sometimes subacute or obtuse; nectaries 8–10, stalked, curved–tubular with an oblique or truncate apex, erose at the margin, green; stamens numerous, erect (? reflexing as they mature); anthers ± circular about 1–1.5 mm diameter; carpels usually 2, rarely 3 but normally only 2 developing into the fruiting stage, basally fused for up to 5 mm, styles straight or somewhat curved at the tips; mature follicles about 1.5 cm long and 1 cm wide; seeds ellipsoid, 3–4 mm long, blackish with a reticulate–pitted testa and a small ridge running along one side.

Flowering time (January–)March–May in the wild.

Habitat Damp shady forest, 1100–3700 metres.

Distribution China, in the provinces of Gansu (Kansu), Shaanxi (Shensi) and Sichuan (Szechuan).

7

The Hellebore cultivars and hybrids

Most of the important work which has been carried out to improve Hellebores as garden plants has involved *H. orientalis* and its variants and, to a lesser extent, some of the purple and green flowered Balkan species. Indeed, the vast majority of 'Lenten Roses' are selections from within the species *H. orientalis*, which I take in a wide sense to include *H. guttatus* and *H. abchasicus* at the rank of subspecies. The colour variation in wild material of this species ranges from nearly pure white through cream (*H. orientalis* subsp. *orientalis*) to pale purple and darker purples, sometimes finely spotted darker (*H. orientalis* subsp. *abchasicus*) or rather conspicuously blotched reddish-purple on a cream or whitish ground (*H. orientalis* subsp. *guttatus*). There appear to be no breeding barriers between these variants of *H. orientalis*, so when brought together in gardens there are numerous possibilities for raising new forms based on flower colour, size and shape. Furthermore the offspring are very fertile so that successive generations can be raised, allowing progressive selection along certain lines, for example towards darker and darker purples or the gradual improvement of a yellow-flowered race.

It is most likely that the early cultivars were mainly selections of *H. orientalis*, dating from the mid 19th century when this and several of its variants were introduced to cultivation in Europe, but it was certainly not long after this that other species were being used to impart various characteristics into the existing 'Lenten Rose' selections and in particular one thinks of the blackish purple form of *H. torquatus* which was in cultivation during this period, certainly as early as 1878 and possibly for some time before this. Cultivars such as 'Afghan Prince' (Barr catalogue 1898), described as a deep slaty purple, and 'Nigricans' (Froebel catalogue 1900) which was indigo blue-black inside and out, must surely have been raised as a result of the influence of one of the darker forms of *H. torquatus* or *H. atrorubens*. Yellows were also being selected at about the same time and in the 1899 catalogue of Barr & Sons can be found such names as 'Caucasicus Lutescens', a rich clear creamy yellow, 'Lividescens Pallidus', creamy yellow, and 'Pallidus', a clear soft primrose yellow. These may well have been hybrids between cream-coloured forms of *H. orientalis* and the yellow-green *H. odorus* or *H. cyclophyllus*, both of which were available in cultivation in the late 19th century.

The Christmas Rose, *H. niger*, does not readily hybridise with the Hellebores of Sect. *Helleborastrum* (i.e. *H. orientalis* etc.) but it does on the other hand cross with the two stemmed species of Hellebore, *H. argutifolius* and *H. lividus*, producing interesting but sterile intermediates (see pages 145, 144), and these two cross freely together giving fertile offspring. *H. foetidus* appears reluctant to hybridise with any other species for, although it is frequently cultivated in association with other Hellebores, I have only two reports of hybrids occurring, one with *H. viridis* (see page 146) and the other an intentional cross involving *H. argutifolius* (see page 145).

H. vesicarius has not to my knowledge been used in hybridisation experiments but has been so rare in cultivation anyway that this is not surprising. There would in fact be little point in using it as a parent, other than for discovering possible genetical relationships, since it is only of moderate aesthetic value, except for the striking inflated fruits. Since any hybrid offspring are likely to be sterile these fruits would probably not be produced, thus defeating the object of hybridisation. Also, the fact that *H. vesicarius* is slightly frost-tender and makes its main growth in winter before dying down for the summer would call into question its suitability as a parent.

H. thibetanus has unfortunately not been introduced to cultivation so whether it will hybridise with other species is not known. Although in its general structural details it is much like the stemless Hellebores of Sect. *Helleborastrum*, pollen studies suggest, surprisingly, that it is more closely related to the caulescent species *H. argutifolius*, *H. lividus* and *H. foetidus*. Crossing experiments would be interesting since they might give some extra clues as to the true relationships of this little-known plant.

We should now look more closely at the two major groups of garden hybrid Hellebores, firstly the most important '*Orientalis* Group' (**A**) and secondly a small but interesting group (**B**, page 141) involving *H. niger*, *H. lividus* and *H. argutifolius*, then the remaining miscellaneous hybrids as Group **C**.

Group A
'*Orientalis* Hybrids' of Sect. *Helleborastrum*

The name *H. × hybridus* Voss (in Vilmorin's *Blumengärtnerei* ed. 3, 1: 25 (1894)) exists for the hybrids of this group. *H. × heyderi* Schiffner refers to crosses between *H. orientalis* subsp. *abchasicus* and subsp. *guttatus*.

These 'Group A hybrids' are derived from *H. orientalis* and its variants *H. guttatus* and *H. abchasicus* (which I am regarding as subspecies). The resulting cultivars have to some extent been crossed with other members of this section, notably with *H. torquatus*, giving darker colours, and with *H. odorus*, *H. cyclophyllus* and possibly *H. multifidus* to introduce yellowish tones.

As indicated above, the history of these dates back to the mid 19th century when the various forms of *H. orientalis* were being brought into cultivation in Europe, mostly via St. Petersburg (Leningrad) Botanic Garden, Berlin Botanic Garden and various nurserymen and private gardeners. It is impossible to trace the exact history since there is no one line of descent to follow, plants being sent on from one horticulturist to another and each conducting his own breeding programmes. Some growers started with the few wild forms available while others acquired already named garden selections and hybrids on which to base their own work. So, in the second half of the 19th century, as is happening now, there were many growers carrying out similar work concurrently, each choosing what they thought to be new and exciting forms and providing cultivar names for them, often in latinised form as if they were species. Inevitably this led to much duplication and confusion and, in the absence of any precise descriptions, it is now impossible to identify most of these early cultivars. This situation has continued now for over a century with the additional fact that the plants have crossed freely by themselves in gardens without the help of man so, as well as the named cultivars, there is a multitude of un-named forms, some aesthetically much better than the named ones!

Although it is more or less impossible to trace the exact ancestry of the 'orientalis hybrids' it is of interest to look at some of the earliest work and mention some of the more important Hellebore breeders of the last 100 years, for among the countless growers who have 'dabbled' in a serendipitous way (and what fun it is!) there are certain individuals and horticultural establishments who have contributed more positively to the improvement of the 'Lenten Rose' hybrids.

One of the earliest references I have found to any serious intentional hybridising concerns the Berlin Botanic Garden in 1851. Carl Koch (1874), speaking of *H. abchasicus* (*H. orientalis* subsp. *abchasicus*) and a darker form of it, which was described as *H. colchicus*, notes that they 'yielded, through cross-fertilization varieties of rare beauty and diversity'. It is worth quoting Koch's next comments in full since they contain valuable historical information:

'To the lamented Mr Sauer, the late superintendent (sic) of the Berlin University Garden, and one of the most intelligent gardeners we have had in Germany, is due the merit of raising hybrids from *H. guttatus* and *H. abchasicus*. His first attempt was made as long ago as 1851, with the two species just named, and proved highly successful, resulting in the production of two series of variations. The plants of the *H. guttatus* series were more vigorous and bore a far greater number of flowers than the type. The flowers of some were bell-shaped, whilst others retained the spreading sepals of the parent species. The dark red spots appeared larger and assumed more of a brown tint. ... The second series of *H. abchasicus* had, for the greater part, paler flowers sometimes with white spots [presumably a mistake! BM], but often destitute of them. .... After some years Mr Sauer saved seed from the prettiest of these varieties, and, as Hellebore seed soon loses its vitality, sowed it at once. The issue was still more brilliant, for in some of the varieties the whole plant, and more especially the flowers, exceed in beauty those of the first sowing. The Minister of Agriculture awarded Mr Sauer the medal for "Progress in Horticulture", then given for the first time. Still further experiments were tried, with the same satisfactory results, each batch adding to the variety. Meanwhile *H. officinalis* (*olympicus*) was introduced into the Botanic Gardens. Above all a variety with blood-red leaves made a great sensation. Mr Bouché, the superintendent of the garden, likewise tried some crosses with this new species, with no less success. The Berlin Botanic Garden possesses a collection of oriental hybrid Hellebores which may with truth be designated as remarkable.'

Koch also noted that in 1874 Carl Heinemann of Erfurt was raising hybrids between *H. guttatus* and *H. abchasicus* and that he was 'much delighted with the beauty of them'. The following year Heinemann sent a box of flowers of hybrid Hellebores to the *Gardeners' Chronicle* and it was reported in a note (*Gardeners' Chronicle* 24th April 1875) that they varied in colour 'from purple to greenish-white, many of the latter flowers are sprinkled with pink dots which give a very striking appearance to the flowers. Some of the sepals are fringed ...'

H. abchasicus was not formally described as a new species until 1853 when A. Braun named it as such from material growing in the Berlin Botanic Garden. It was however catalogued in 1852 by James Booth & Son of Hamburg, so it would appear that the species must have been available for some time before this in order for saleable quantities to be built up. It seems to me likely that the first hybrids in Germany were produced in the 1840s since *H. guttatus* had been collected by Koch in 1837, and *H. abchasicus* had been introduced some time before 1852. The white *H. orientalis* from Turkey, which appears to have arrived in Britain in 1840, was also cultivated in the Berlin Botanic Garden in the early 1850s but may well have been introduced from the Caucasus some years before this. Thus, all the elements for a breeding programme involving the variants of *H. orientalis* were available, certainly in Germany, by the middle of the 19th century. During the next 20 years there was clearly much activity in the selection and crossing of Hellebores, the material being distributed widely in Europe, to several renowned horticulturists such as Carl Heinemann of Erfurt, Max Leichtlin of Baden Baden and Otto Froebel of Zürich, all of these and others in France and Belgium producing a range of cultivars. In England some of the leading names were Peter Barr of Barr & Sugden, later to become Barr & Sons of Covent Garden, Thomas Archer-Hind of Coombe Fishacre (sometimes written Coombefishacre) in Devon and the Canon H.N. Ellacombe in Bitton in Gloucestershire; all had large and varied collections of Hellebores in the 1870s. Specimens at Kew, mainly from the herbarium of Thomas Moore of Chelsea which was purchased by Kew in 1887, show that these three plantsmen all possessed a wide range in 1877 and were developing their own varieties.

Peter Rudolph Barr (1826–1909) was a noted nurseryman whose main contribution to horticulture was in the breeding of Daffodils, the collection being grown at Tooting in the 1860s and later on in Surbiton, Surrey. The latter site near the railway station was advertised in 1893 as having a grand display of 2 million Daffodils in 500 varieties. However, it is the hardy herbaceous perennials which are of interest to us and we find from the catalogues that there was a wide collection of these, especially Hellebores, in the 1880s. There is good evidence in the form of herbarium specimens that Barr acquired plants from various sources including Heinemann and Max Leichtlin in Germany. In an article in the *Gardeners' Chronicle* of April 1880 it is stated that in Barr's Tooting nursery there were some new Hellebore varieties which had been bought from Leichtlin as unflowered seedlings; several had been selected out and given cultivar names such as 'Peter Rudolph Barr', 'Punctatissimus' and 'Arthur Collins'. Barr was also exchanging with other growers nearer to home including Archer-Hind, Ellacombe and Moore in Dublin. Thomas Archer-Hind wrote in *The Garden* of 1884 that Mr Barr's collection 'is by far the most extensive in existence', but from the information I have gleaned it seems that no one person was well to the fore in Hellebore breeding and that all were exchanging, hybridising and selecting at much the same period. We can roughly pinpoint the date of the start of Barr's activity in this field from his catalogue of 1890 which states that he had been working on Hellebore selection for 20 years, presumably starting with material imported from Germany since clearly this was the major source of the species and early hybrids from 1850 onwards. Possibly some also came direct from St. Petersburg (Leningrad), as this was an important staging post in the dissemination of Caucasian material, via the great plantsman-botanist Regel.

Barr & Sons amassed a magnificent collection of Hellebores consisting of the *orientalis* hybrids, which were grouped together in the catalogues on account of their overwintering leaves, *H. niger* in a fine array of different forms, and a third group which contained those with deciduous leaves, mainly Balkan species. The 'Hardy Herbaceous Perennial' list for 1889 (prices were of the order of 6 plants for 10s 6d* = about 50p) gives us a good idea of the wide range available and is worth repeating. I have amended it slightly, putting many of the names in single quotes where I think they were intended to represent cultivar names rather than species.

Barr & Sons 1889
Orientalis hybrids with old leaves remaining through winter

abchasicus – rose purple
antiquorum – large pale purple
'Apotheker Bogren' – rich purple rose
caucasicus – greenish white
caucasicus 'Sulphureus' – yellow
'Commerzienrath Benary' – white spotted crimson
colchicus – deep plum, young leaves purplish
colchicus 'Coccineus' – richer coloured form of above
colchicus 'Punctatus' – deep plum, spotted all over interior
'Frau Irene Heinemann' – purple-rose, spotted carmine red
'Gertrude Jekyll' – pure white
guttatus – white spotted crimson in centre
guttatus 'Leichtlinii' – white profusely spotted crimson
guttatus 'Subpunctatus' – pure white
'Hofgarten–Inspektor Hartwig' – plum purple, moderately spotted
'Lividescens' – pale dull purple, tinged green inside
olympicus – white
olympicus 'Professor Schleicher' – white
orientalis – white, large
orientalis 'Olban Otto' – white
'Pallidus' – white, small flower
'Peter Rudolph Barr' – red-purple, spotted all over inside
'Punctatus' – purple, freely spotted inside
'Punctatissimus' – bright rose purple, inside profusely spotted
'Roseus' – deep rose
'Roseus Punctatus' – deep rose, freely spotted inside
'Ruberissimus' – reddish purple with red stems

---

* This was just over half the wage a gardener would earn per week.
(*Gardeners' Chronicle* of the time)

H. niger varieties

niger
- " 'Maximus' – large rose tinted flowers, large dark green leaves
- " 'Major' – large flowers
- " 'Minor'
- " 'The Bath'
- " 'Scoticus' – (Miss Hope's Christmas Rose)
- " 'Caucasicus' – snow white, outside tinged rose, fragrant
- " 'Madame Fourcade' – large pure white
- " 'Rubra' – rosy white, outside purple-red, late
- " 'Foliis Variegatis'

Leaves disappearing in winter

bocconei – large bright green, elder scented
dumetorum – small green
graveolens – tinged brown-purple, inside green
intermedius – outside dove purple, inside green
'Luridus' – tinged brown-purple, inside green, foliage elegantly divided
purpurascens – green tinged purple
torquatus – dwarf with beautiful dove-coloured flowers
viridis – large white-green

Also added to the list were *H. foetidus* and *H. lividus*.

The selection in the Barr catalogues varied in the succeeding years with new named varieties appearing, some obviously imported from Europe (e.g. 'Otto Froebel', 'Bismark') and by 1897 there were 40 varieties of *H. orientalis* alone, while two years later 50 were catalogued, including 'Afghan Prince', described as a deep slaty purple, 'Brutus', a coppery rose, 'Tom Thumb', a dwarf variety with flowers of a delicate rose pink shading to yellow, 'Dr Hogg', rich deep rose, and 'Psyche', soft pink with a crimson blotch at the base of each segment. Each year there were slight changes to the list and after Peter Barr's retirement the firm continued through the 1920s, 30s and 40s to offer an excellent array of Hellebores from the nursery at Taplow near Maidenhead. Noteworthy varieties offered in the later catalogues included 'Black Knight' (RHS Award of Merit 1926), with blackish-crimson flowers and dark bronze foliage, and 'Coombe Fishacre Purple', a rosy purple one raised by T. Archer-Hind. A few of those named are still in cultivation, for example 'White Swan' and 'Queen of the North' which are to be seen at Kew, but although of historical interest they are not outstandingly beautiful and are equalled if not surpassed by some of the modern cultivars. Undoubtedly Peter Barr was a leading figure in England in the development and distribution of the Hellebore via his famous nursery.

One must not however forget that there were other nurserymen in England breeding and supplying Hellebore hybrids. Hale Farm Nursery of Tottenham was also distributing named cultivars resulting from crosses between *H. olympicus*, *H.*

colchicus and *H. guttatus* and one of these was called 'Thomas S. Ware' after the owner, a well-known horticulturist of the 1880s.

Thomas Hodgson Archer-Hind was known in his family as 'The Hellebore Man' and was a contemporary of Peter Barr. It is clear from his writings that the two were in close contact over matters concerning Hellebores, and they certainly exchanged plants. In 1871 Archer-Hind started a garden at Coombe Fishacre near Newton Abbott in Devon where he grew and selected new varieties, some of which were named after the garden, such as 'Coombe Fishacre Purple' and 'Coombe Fishacre Yellow'. Archer-Hind's Hellebores were painted by his wife during 1879 and 1881 and these illustrations still exist in the possession of Mrs Gillian Raymond, her great granddaughter. From the botanical point of view T.H. Archer-Hind will be remembered, since he described and named *H. torquatus* in *The Garden* of 8th March 1884. His description is sufficiently comprehensive to identify the plant as the blackish-purple flowered Hellebore which occurs in southern Yugoslavia, later to be called *H. serbicus* or *H. multifidus* subsp. *serbicus*, and much-confused with *H. purpurascens*. *H. torquatus* is however by far the oldest name for the species and must take priority. Archer-Hind was apparently not aware of the original source of the plant but he had known it as a garden plant for several years prior to 1884. Exactly when it was introduced is not recorded as far as I can ascertain but it was listed in a few catalogues of the period showing that it too was available to the early breeders of Hellebores. This is important, for it gives a clue to the likely origin of the very dark colours in some of the *orientalis* hybrids which we now know can be achieved by using *H. torquatus* as a parent. One particular line of breeding followed by Thomas Archer-Hind was to produce a range of '*H. guttatus* hybrids' using as a parent the Caucasian plant which has red-spotted flowers, but his work appears to have had no bounds and E.B. Anderson (1957), who acquired a collection of Archer-Hind hybrids, noted that there was 'a range from pure white through cream to pink and lilac and on to deep maroon and crimson. Some unspotted, some with large spots on a white or pink ground, others peppered with small dots. Most of them are cup-shaped with overlapping tepals, others show the more pointed tepals of some of the species'. The yellow-flowered seedlings which Archer-Hind selected, known as 'Coombe Fishacre Yellow' and 'Primrose Dame' were, according to Mr Anderson who had seen them, probably *H. orientalis* × *H. guttatus*, and not very yellow.

The Rev. Henry N. Ellacombe's name is also closely associated with hellebores. He was vicar of Bitton church near Bristol from 1850 onwards and was, judging by the biographical accounts, a quite exceptional man, both in his profession and in his many other interests, of which gardening was but one. An overriding quality seems to have been his generosity and an extract from a letter shows what pleasure he gained from giving: 'If I give a friend 100 plants and he gives me one, I thank him for his one, but I don't enter him as my debtor for ninety-nine'. His garden became a mecca for plantsmen and no less a person than E.A. Bowles once remarked that the Bitton garden was the most interesting he had ever seen. Ellacombe's writings in the gardening press were extensive and he published several books, including *In a Gloucestershire Garden* (1895), *In my Vicarage Garden and Elsewhere* (1902) and *The Plant Lore and Garden Craft of Shakespeare* (1878) which was a perfect topic for a classical scholar with a special interest in Shakespeare and a love of plants! Ellacombe certainly grew and distributed a lot of Hellebore hybrids but whether he was responsible for breeding some of his own I do not know. In 1895 he wrote 'I also grow and am fond of the many hybrids raised about thirty years ago (chiefly at Berlin) between *H. guttatus* and *H. abchasicus*', perhaps indicating that he did not in fact do a great deal of his own selecting. There is firm evidence from herbarium specimens at Kew and Wisley dated 1877 that he received plants direct from A. Braun at Berlin Botanic Garden including *H. abchasicus*, *H. caucasicus* 'Punctatus' (a form of *H. abchasicus*), *H.* 'Albido-Virescens', *H.* 'Reticulatus', *H.* 'Porphyromelas' (an *H. abchasicus* form), *H.* 'Pallidus', *H.* 'Pallidus Albus' and *H.* 'Punctatus Hybrids'. Soon after this, in March or April 1879, Ellacombe sent a collection of flowers of Hellebore cultivars to the *Gardeners' Chronicle* and these were seen by Thomas Moore who wrote an article for the *Chronicle* of 5th April 1879, comparing Ellacombe's plants with those of Barr and Sons. There is nothing in the article to suggest that any of the names mentioned were provided by Ellacombe but he was undoubtedly instrumental in popularising the genus in Britain at that time.

In Ireland, at Glasnevin Botanic Garden, there was also much interest in Hellebores during the 19th century, some being imported from England, others from Europe, and these forming the stock for further hybridisation and selection. Many of them were illustrated by Lydia Shackleton during the years 1885 to 1888 and the paintings are now housed in the National Botanic Gardens, Glasnevin. These are a valuable record since some of the older cultivars are represented, such as 'Dr Moore' (after David Moore of Glasnevin), 'Peter R. Barr', 'Apotheker Bogren', 'F.J. Heinemann', 'Commerzienrath Benary' and 'Punctatissimus'. Those raised in the Gardens during the time of Sir Frederick Moore included some yellowish ones, 'Luteus Grandiflorus' and 'Yellow Seedling', and Charles Nelson, in his delightful book *An Irish Flower Garden* (1984), relates the story of how in 1921 Sir Frederick sent a collection of Hellebores from Glasnevin to E.A. Bowles of Myddleton House, Enfield. 'Luteus Grandiflorus' was included among these and it did well at Myddleton so that by 1957 it had formed, according to E.B. Anderson, a large plant which stood out strikingly against a dark background. From the garden of E.A. Bowles a vegetative propagation of it reached the RHS Garden at Wisley where I saw it in the 1960s. It probably represents a selection from the cream forms of *H. orientalis*, for I can find no evidence for it being of hybrid origin. It has no suggestion of scent and the leaves are not particularly hairy on the undersides; were it a hybrid between *H. orientalis* and *H. cyclophyllus* or *H. odorus* (as are most of the modern yellows) I would expect to find both of these features represented to some extent, plus a few other characteristics. It is perhaps rather more of a yellowish green than pure yellow and has now been exceeded in yellowness by some of the more recent selections, but nevertheless it is a pleasing plant and is historically interesting. Graham Stuart Thomas has a similar plant which he calls 'Bowles' Yellow', possibly part of the same stock which originated in Glasnevin.

There is of course no break in continuity between the Hellebore breeding of the 19th and 20th centuries. Barr and Sons were still very actively engaged in selecting and naming cultivars for most of the first half of this century, and many other people as well. 'Black Knight' and 'Prince Rupert', exhibited by Barr, received Awards of Merit in 1926 and 1927 respectively and show that the firm had retained their interest in the genus for nearly half a century. It is difficult to draw a line between the people who possessed excellent collections of Hellebores and those who actively tried to improve the range of cultivars. Good collections were, or are, to be found in many a garden and one can think of names such as E.B Anderson, Mrs Amy Doncaster, Mrs Margery Fish, Norman Hadden, Eliot Hodgkin, Miss Nancy Lindsay, Mrs Maxted, Netta Statham and Sir Frederick Stern, all keen Hellebore enthusiasts. In the 1960s I spent a few months working at Highdown in Sussex and at that time Sir Frederick Stern was selecting those seedlings which held their flowers up horizontally rather than drooping, a particular line which a number of people have attempted to follow. He was also the proud possessor of what was apparently a piece of the original Archer-Hind blackish *H. torquatus* and I can confirm that this was the same species, and indeed almost the same form of it, as that which I saw a few years earlier in the Ingwersen nursery, introduced in 1929 by Walter Ingwersen from southern Yugoslavia.

E.B. Anderson did a considerable amount of hybridisation, including some experiments which added weight to the view that none of the stemless Hellebores of section *Helleborastrum* would cross with *H. niger*. More importantly, he did much to popularise the species Hellebores through his lecture to the RHS on 30 April 1957, subsequently published in the Journal for July 1957.

In more recent times there have been many Hellebore enthusiasts, both private growers and nurserymen, who have done a great deal of valuable work, and one must mention here Eric Smith who teamed up with Jim Archibald to form the fascinating hardy plant nursery in Dorset known as The Plantsmen. This partnership produced and distributed a fine range of cultivars, many of them named after heavenly bodies. Particularly noteworthy were the *H. torquatus* × *H. orientalis* hybrids, such as the famous 'Pluto', and some improved yellows of which 'Sirius' was particularly good and vigorous. They also used as one of the parents a form of *H. orientalis* with dark red nectaries (this must have been a variant of subsp. *abchasicus*) and this feature was carried through to the offspring, sometimes with very pleasing results. A particular Smith-Archibald favourite of mine is 'Orion' which has a creamy sulphur flower with dark purple nectaries and purple stain at the base of each perianth segment forming an eye in the centre. Although 'The Plantsmen' no longer exists as a nursery, quite a number of their Hellebore introductions are being maintained in cultivation and are holding their position as some of the finest cultivars ever raised.

One of the most remarkable collections of Hellebores in existence belongs to Mrs Helen Ballard who runs a small specialist nursery near Malvern. Her late husband Philip was primarily interested in *Galanthus* and owned a fine collection of interesting varieties. His father Ernest, although world famous as a breeder of Michaelmas Daisies, will also be remembered for the very dark 'Ballard's Black' Hellebore, a rich dark purple form which became one of the classical cultivars of our time although sadly now extremely rare. Helen Ballard began her Hellebore breeding in about 1965 with only a few *H. orientalis* forms, from which through hybridisation and selection she has raised a great range of colours. The crossing of a cream *H. orientalis* form (*H. olympicus*) with a green-flowered species (probably *H. multifidus* subsp. *istriacus*) collected by her and her husband in NW Yugoslavia, has led to a race of good yellows, some individual clones of which have been named, such as 'Citron', 'Ingot' and 'Yellow Button'. In the darker colours Mrs Ballard has produced an extraordinary range using *H. torquatus* to introduce a definite bluish-black tone into the already dark *H. orientalis* forms. 'Blue Wisp' and 'Philip Ballard' are two of the most exciting in this particular range and probably represent some of the darkest cultivars ever produced, although we unfortunately cannot assess some of the older European forms such as 'Nigricans' which is said to have been blackish. Mrs Ballard has also worked for some years on *H. niger* × *H. lividus* crosses (see page 144) and grows the largest Christmas Roses I have ever seen, both in terms of flower size and in general vigour.

Washfield Nursery near Hawkhurst, Kent must also be included in any account of modern hellebore breeding since its owner, Elizabeth Strangman, has developed an excellent yellow-flowered race using *H. odorus* and *H. cyclophyllus* crossed with *H. orientalis* forms. Other fine cultivars include the best white *H. orientalis* I have seen, with large perfectly formed rounded flowers, clear pink shades with no trace of spotting, a range of deep blackish-purple colours and an extraordinary *H. viridis* × *H. orientalis* subsp. *guttatus* hybrid with green flowers spotted red inside. Miss Strangman has also discovered double-flowered forms of *H. torquatus* in the wild (see page 100) and has brought together some other doubles from various sources to add to what currently must be one of the finest collections of species and hybrids in the country.

Before leaving this section, which is devoted to the 'Orientalis hybrids', I should also mention Will McLewin who is presently enthusiastically hybridising and selection out an interesting range of Hellebores.

Those individuals I have included in this account are of course only a selection of the people who have been or are involved in Hellebore breeding and unfortunately I am almost certain to have omitted someone who has done some important work; to them I apologise.

Group B
Hybrids involving *H. niger*, *H. argutifolius* and *H. lividus*

(a) *Helleborus* × *sternii* Turrill in Bot. Mag. 171, t. 291 (1957)

Synonym
H. lividus notosubsp. *sternii* (Turrill) Yeo in Taxon 35: 157 (1986).

Parentage
H. argutifolius Viv. ('*H. corsicus*') × *H. lividus* Aiton

Whenever the two stemmed species of Hellebore, *H. argutifolius* and *H. lividus*, are brought together in gardens they are likely to hybridise producing a range of fertile intermediates. These were first recorded in the 1940s in Sir Frederick Stern's garden at Highdown in Sussex and were given the name *H.* × *sternii* by Dr Turrill, who deposited a specimen of the original plant in the

Kew Herbarium. The hybrids vary enormously in stature, from rather stocky plants resembling *H. lividus* with dark green leaves veined cream on the upper surface and suffused beneath with purple, through to more robust ones with paler leaves resembling *H. argutifolius*. The margins of the leaflets may be almost lacking in teeth, as in *H. lividus*, or they may be prominently spiny-toothed like those of *H. argutifolius*, with almost every possible intermediate version. The flowers of *H. × sternii* normally have a certain amount of purplish-brown staining derived from *H. lividus* and there are generally fewer in each inflorescence than there are in *H. argutifolius*. The hybrid seems to be equally successful whether *H. lividus* or *H. argutifolius* is used as the seed parent, and the resulting offspring are fertile.

Some selections of *H. × sternii* variants have been made and particularly attractive is 'Boughton Beauty'. This was raised by Valerie Finnis (Lady Scott) and named after Boughton House, Kettering, Northants, from seeds sent to her by Ken Aslet when he was Superintendent of the Wisley rock garden. Although having marked characteristics of *H. lividus*, a compact habit, attractively marked leaves and a pinkish-purple suffusion throughout, it is clear that this is a hybrid and inherits some of the hardiness and vigour of its Corsican parent. Another noteworthy variant of *H. × sternii* has been raised by Mr A.R. White of Blackthorn Nursery, Alresford, Hampshire. This is known as 'Blackthorn Strain' and like the previous one also has compact growth, but in this case the leaves are a lead-coloured greyish-green and the flowers are slightly flushed with pink. If isolated, individual variants of *H. × sternii*, such as 'Boughton Beauty', appear to breed fairly true to form from seed.

(b) *H. × nigercors* J.T. Wall in Gard. Chron. ser. 3, 96: 427, fig. 166 (1934).

Parentage
H. argutifolius Viv. × *H. niger* L.

In 1931 Mr J.E.H. Stooke of Danesmere, Hereford, exhibited at one of the RHS shows a hybrid between *H. niger* and what was at one time called *H. corsicus*. The Scientific Committee suggested the name *H. nigericors*, but a description of the plant under this epithet was never published and it was not until 1934 in the *Gardeners' Chronicle* of 15th December that a name with a description appeared, with the slightly modified spelling of *H. × nigercors* which should therefore be taken as the correct form of the name. Another mis-spelling is '*nigricors*'. It is unfortunate that *corsicus* appears in the make-up of the name since the Corsican Hellebore should correctly be called *H. argutifolius*.

Apart from the original hybrid of 1931, which had *H. niger* as the seed parent, the cross has been repeated on several occasions with a certain amount of variation in the resulting offspring, partly caused by the fact that the two parents are variable, *H. niger* particularly so. E.B. Anderson (1957) records that the plant he had of the original clone died out in 1954 and that his own attempts at repeating the cross had failed. However, a chance seedling arose in the Hawkhurst garden of Miss Hilda Davenport-Jones and this was exhibited by Mr

Anderson at the RHS show of 8 March 1960 as *H. × nigericors* 'Hawkhurst'. In 1958 E.B. Anderson did succeed in obtaining 15 seeds from his own crossing experiments but remarked that only one of the resulting seedlings was obviously of hybrid origin. This plant was eventually named 'Beatrix' after his wife and received a Preliminary Commendation on 7th February 1967 when shown by Mr Anderson. Also in 1967, Miss Davenport-Jones repeated the cross and obtained four seedlings, one of which flowered in 1969 and was subsequently named 'Alabaster'. This fine plant had *H. niger* 'Potter's Wheel' as the seed parent and is probably the best of the *H. × nigercors* seedlings so far raised. It was given an A.M. in 1971 and has been illustrated in the RHS Journal of March 1972 and more recently in the *Kew Magazine* 4, 4: t. 85 (1987). Elizabeth Strangman, now the owner of Washfield Nursery, continues to propagate this excellent plant, as well as raising new *H. niger × H. argutifolius* seedlings.

It is difficult to track down all the hybrids of this parentage since there appear to have been quite a number of successful attempts. There is an article and a photograph in the RHS Journal of July 1975 by A. Sigston Thompson in which he describes how he received a batch of seeds of *H. niger × H. argutifolius* (*H. corsicus*) from a friend and grew on several, noting that it was a 'most startlingly attractive winter flowering plant'. Currently Mr A.R. White of Blackthorn Nursery, Alresford, Hampshire, is raising *H. × nigercors* from seed, and I recently received an extremely vigorous large-flowered specimen for identification from Mrs Eileen Sweeting, from a plant raised by the late Edgar Ellis of Osset, Yorkshire. As far as I can ascertain most, if not all, of the *H. × nigercors* hybrids have *H. niger* as the seed parent.

Clearly if one of the caulescent species, which has the flowers in clusters at the apex of a leafy stem, is hybridised with the acaulescent *H. niger*, which produces its flowers on separate non-leafy stems, the resulting offspring will be fairly unusual in the way in which the flowers are borne. *H. × nigercors* has short tough stems carrying the leaves and terminal clusters of flowers but in addition there are some basal leaves, and flowers produced on short stalks around the base of the plant. Sometimes there are extra flowers produced in the leaf axils, so this can be a very floriferous plant when growing well. The flowers are large, flattish and white with a hint of green, rather closer in appearance to those of *H. niger* than the smaller-cupped green ones of *H. argutifolius*, but the leaves are truly intermediate. In the plant of 'Alabaster' figured in the *Kew Magazine* some leaves were trifoliolate, with a tendency for at least one of the leaflets to divide into shallow lobes, while others were distinctly pedate with the two lateral leaflets deeply divided into two, giving a total of five segments; all the leaves had very coarse jagged teeth on the margins. There is some variation in leaf characters between the various crosses which have been made. The one illustrated and described in the *Gardeners' Chronicle* of 1934 had pedate leaves with up to seven segments while the one exhibited at the 1967 RHS show by E.B. Anderson had trifoliolate spiny-edged leaves more like those of *H. argutifolius*.

The fact that *H. niger* will hybridise with *H. argutifolius* is rather surprising since it does not appear at first to be closely related to any other species and is placed in a section of its own (see pages 66 & 67).

A short while ago I would have said that there were no authenticated cases of *H. niger* hybridising with another species, apart from *H. argutifolius* (and *H.*

lividus), but recently I heard of a *H. niger* × *H. viridis* cross (see page 146). *H. argutifolius* will apparently only readily hybridise with *H. niger*, although here again there is a convincing report of an intentional *H. argutifolius* × *H. foetidus* cross (see page 145). It seems likely that *H. niger* and *H. argutifolius* are genetically somewhat more closely related to each other than they are to *Helleborus* species of the other sections, although morphologically they are very different.

As a garden plant *H.* × *nigercors* appears to require a fairly rich soil in a partially shaded site. It is known to have succeeded in fairly heavy alkaline soils and in acid sandy ones so is apparently tolerant of a wide range of conditions. It is a sterile hybrid so in order to perpetuate it either the cross must be repeated or individuals must be vegetatively propagated. Hybrid seedlings can be obtained fairly readily using *H. niger* as the seed parent and they grow quite rapidly, sometimes flowering in 1 or 2 years from germination. Alternatively *H.* × *nigercors* may be increased by division, making sure that each piece of rhizome has a shoot and good roots. Although this is a fairly slow method, the plants are of course identical with their parent.

(c) *H. niger* L. × *H. lividus* Aiton

The result of crossing *H. niger* and *H. lividus* is a range of interesting intermediates with large flattish white flowers tinged with pinkish-brown or pinkish-purple, changing to a dull purple throughout as they age. The plants are stocky, no more than 30 cm in height, with short stems bearing a few terminal flowers. The leaves, which are somewhere between pedate and trifoliolate, usually have 5–7 divisions on the plants I have seen, and they are deep green with creamy veining, a feature derived from *H. lividus*. Mrs Helen Ballard has done a considerable amount of work in producing hybrids between the two species and some of her cultivars were exhibited at an RHS show in 1973 under the names 'December Dawn' and 'Midwinter'. The former had flowers 6–8 cm in diameter, while those of the latter were even larger, at about 9 cm across. The bracts, as one might expect of a cross between these two very different plants were also intermediate, the upper ones being undivided like those of *H. niger* while the lower ones had small leaf-like divisions at the apex, as does *H. lividus*. As far as I know the cross has only been successfully made using *H. niger* as the seed parent. The hybrid is undoubtedly hardier than *H. lividus*, for one specimen I have growing in the open garden has survived several winters, including the severe one of 1986–87, whereas my *H. lividus* plants have not survived any of our recent winters. However the plant of *H. niger* × *H. lividus* which I have in a large pot in a frost-free greenhouse is far superior to the one outdoors and shows that this hybrid is an attractive winter-flowering subject for the conservatory or unheated greenhouse.

(d) *H. niger* L. × *H.* × *sternii* Turrill

Not surprisingly, if *H. niger* will cross with *H. argutifolius* and *H. lividus*, it will also cross with their fertile offspring *H.* × *sternii*. Plants with this parentage were raised and distributed by Eric Smith and Jim Archibald, whose nursery 'The Plantsmen' was the source of many other fine plants, including a range of *H. orientalis* hybrids (see page 145). The name '*H.* × *nigristern*' has become attached to the offspring of liaisons between these two plants but although this is usefully informative about the parentage of the hybrid, it is a name which will be frowned upon by those who follow the International Code of Nomenclature.

Obviously the *H. niger* × *H.* × *sternii* hybrids vary greatly in their appearance depending upon which particular form of the variable *H.* × *sternii* has been used. However, most of those I have seen are quite short with large white flowers tinged on the outside with pinkish-brown or green, becoming more strongly coloured with age. The somewhat pedately divided leaves show a little of the attractive pale veining of *H. lividus*.

Group C
Miscellaneous Hellebore hybrids

(1) *H.* × *jourdanii* Pagès (*H. foetidus* L × *H. viridis* L.)

E. Pagès, in Bull. Geog. Bot. 24: 167 (1914) reported finding a plant of this parentage in a mixed population in France at St. Amans-de-Mounis. He gives a fairly convincing comparative table of characters.

In a letter to me dated 15 February 1967, Tony Venison, Gardening Editor of *Country Life*, wrote 'Whilst in north central Spain last June ... we discovered an area of the road between Soria and Logrono where populations of *H. foetidus* and *H. viridis* overlapped and there were many apparent hybrids'. I have not seen such hybrids myself so cannot comment further.

These are the only records I have found of crosses between Section *Griphopus* and Section *Helleborastrum*.

(2) *H. argutifolius* Viv. (*H. corsicus* Willd.) × *H. foetidus* L.

In the *Canadian Journal of Genetics and Cytology* 8; 516 (1966), M.J. Harvey gives an account of some work done at Durham University using plants growing in the Botanic Garden. He writes: 'In 1960 hopes of producing horticulturally desirable specimens led to attempts being made to make hybrids between five species (*H. atrorubens* Waldst. & Kit., *H. corsicus* Willd., *H. foetidus* L., *H. niger* L. and *H. viridis* L.) but for various reasons the only mature hybrid plants obtained were *H. corsicus* × *foetidus*.' *H. argutifolius* (*H. corsicus*) was the seed parent and the resulting seeds germinated in 1961 and flowered in spring of their third year. Dr. Harvey continues that 'The hybrids were morphologically intermediate but grew vigorously and produced large tall plants which unfortunately were not as decorative as the *H. corsicus* parent'. He noted that the pollen of the hybrids was badly formed and non-functional, so presumably the plants were sterile.

This constitutes the only record of a hybrid between Sections *Griphopus* and *Chenopus*.

(3) *H. niger* L. × *H. viridis* L.

Mr Jeremy Wood of White Parish near Salisbury tells me that he has obtained a seedling from an intentional cross between *H. niger* and *H. viridis*, but the plant is very weak and has made an abortive attempt at flowering. The fact that this hybrid plant is reluctant to grow probably supports the view that *H. niger* should be placed in its own section away from the other 'stemless' Hellebores of section *Helleborastrum*. The weakness of the hybrid may well be an indication of a marked degree of incompatibility.

(4) *H. multifidus* Vis. (?subsp. *istriacus*) × *H. orientalis* Lam. subsp. *guttatus* (A.Br. & Sauer) B. Mathew

A specimen deposited in the Herbarium at the RHS Garden, Wisley in 1977, reputedly having the above parentage, does look convincing. The leaves have all their leaflets divided into at least two segments (a *multifidus* feature) but the plant has large (at least 6 cm diameter) greenish-white flowers spotted with red. Although it is not surprising that these two will hybridise, since both are members of section *Helleborastrum*, it is the only example I have seen of one of the more cut-leaved versions of *H. multifidus* being used in hybridisation. It would be interesting to try the extremely dissected leaved variant, *H. multifidus* subsp. *hercegovinus*, as a parent in an effort to enhance the foliage of the *H. orientalis* cultivars.

(5) *H. niger* L. × *H. orientalis* Lam.

I have heard of and read reports of *H. niger* crossing with *H. orientalis* to produce plants with large white flowers, but there is no clear evidence to support this. The only specimens I have seen of reputed hybrids have proved to be merely good white forms of *H. orientalis* or *H. niger*.

(6) *H. niger* L. × *H. purpurascens* Waldst. & Kit.

In 1874, Carl Koch noted in the *Gardeners' Chronicle* that 'Randonnet of Hyères undertook experiments about ten years ago ... with *H. niger* and *H. purpurascens*, and succeeded in raising some hybrids'. Unfortunately one cannot check back on the identity of the parent plants, nor of the offspring so it is impossible to comment upon the authenticity of this report.

Double Hellebores

Various 'double-flowered' hellebores have appeared from time to time. Semi-double would be a better term since the centre still contains a mass of stamens, the extra sepals being a result of the nectaries mutating. As yet there has been no really double Hellebore, to the extent of the fully double Peonies and Ranunculus, for example. I have mentioned elsewhere the double forms of *H. torquatus* which were found in the wild by Miss Elizabeth Strangman. Portions of these plants were brought into cultivation at Washfield Nursery and have been given cultivar names, 'Dido' for the one which is purplish on the outside and 'Aeneas', which is mainly green with a tinge of brownish-purple on the exterior. Surprisingly, some

Helleborus rhizome

H. multifidus showing carpels fused at base

H. orientalis showing carpels free at base

Detail of the pedate leaf of *H. foetidus* showing the undivided central leaflet and the two lateral ones subdivided

Comparison of leaves of *H. viridis* (left) and *H. dumetorum* (right)

Leaves of the three Balkan purple-flowered species. Top left, *H. purpurascens*; top right *H. torquatus*; bottom *H. atrorubens*

double-flowered seedlings have been raised from 'Dido' including a pinkish form, 'Belinda'.

Another double, which appears to be a purple *H. orientalis* form, arose by chance at Hidcote Manor, Gloucestershire, and was noticed by Graham Stuart Thomas who propagated and distributed it. In a letter dated 6 May 1987 he told me that 'the double purple Hellebore was a self sown seedling at Hidcote ... if you want a name for it I suggest 'Hidcote Double''.

A most interesting double form which I have seen recently in Elizabeth Strangman's nursery is a pinkish-purple form with prominent spotting. This came to her from Germany via Herr Klose and was raised by Fa. Jürgl of Cologne.

H. niger has also been reported with double flowers, and such a form was once found growing wild at Scheibbs in Austria by a Mr Koeppen. Interestingly, it was noted that the stamens were white and petaloid whereas it seems that in all the other double forms I have seen it is the nectaries which have reverted into sepal-like structures.

A plant of *H. viridis* in my own garden in Surrey has produced semi-double flowers and single on the same plant but is not reliable so it seems that this is some sort of seasonal 'hiccup' rather than a more permanent gene-controlled peculiarity. Richard Nutt of Bradenham, Bucks. also sent me a specimen of *H. viridis* in 1985 which had two single flowers and one semi-double on the same stem.

Since at least some of the seedlings of double forms appear to come true to form it seems likely that this is a feature which could be introduced by hybridisation into a wider range of cultivars, perhaps in time leading to a race of more tightly double-flowered forms.

8

Cultivation

Although I have commented about specific needs under each of the Helleborus species it is convenient to combine the cultivation notes into one chapter and make various general comments which are not made elsewhere.

Firstly, a word about the conditions they experience in the wild is in order since this may give clues to their successful cultivation. Hellebores occur usually in the semi-shade of deciduous trees and shrubs in fairly heavy soils over limestone formations, although *H. orientalis* is generally found on acid soils. In spring the soil may be very wet – I have seen *H. viridis* and *H. torquatus* in stiff clay only a few feet away from streams – but in the summer months it dries out considerably, either because there is much less rainfall or because the trees and shrubs are extracting large amounts of moisture from the soil at that time of year. In winter the Hellebores may be in damp conditions if at low altitudes or covered by snow on the mountains. At the cooler higher altitudes they tend to grow more out in the open so, for example, it is possible to find *H. foetidus*, which is a woodland plant in Britain, growing out on exposed rocky hillsides in the mountains of Spain. *H. cyclophyllus* abandons its scrubland and moves out on to grassy mountain sides in southern Yugoslavia, and I have seen *H. niger* looking most odd in the eastern Alps as it pushed its large white flowers through the dead subalpine grass in early spring. These however are exceptions and on the whole Helleborus species are best treated as plants for the semi-shade. As woodland plants they naturally receive a certain amount of top dressing of leaves each year and I am sure that it is a good policy in the garden to prepare the soil in advance of planting by digging in leafmould. I have never seen Hellebores growing in soil which could be described as peaty and I am certain that leafmould or well-rotted garden compost is infinitely preferable to peat when supplying them with humus. If leafmould is impossible to obtain, the light sphagnum moss peat should be used rather than one of the darker sedge peats.

In the garden Hellebores are fairly tolerant of a wide range of soil types providing that they are not very dry or waterlogged. The incorporation of humus in the form of leafmould will improve both these extremes, leading to better water-retention in dry sandy soils and better drainage on heavy clay ones. The best collections of *Helleborus* species seem to have been associated with near-neutral or alkaline soils so the application of ground limestone or chalk to acid soils is to be recommended. The vigorous *H. orientalis* is however an exception and its hybrids are very tolerant of a wide range of conditions and will thrive in most gardens regardless of soil type, although, here again, waterlogged and extremely dry places should be avoided. Hellebores will also fail to do well if in too much shade, usually flowering rather sparsely or not at all rather than actually dying, so make sure that they receive dappled sunlight or sun for at least part of the day.

Hardiness. Most Hellebores are tough and will stand European and North American winters without any problems. They are naturally spring-flowering plants and in the colder regions they tend to stay dormant longer and come into growth when the worst of the weather is finished. Climates such as that of England are kind in that the winters are relatively mild but may cause problems by being unreliable, with long frost-free spells encouraging early growth, then sharp frosts causing damage to the young shoots. I have even seen the English native *H. viridis* blackened by the biting winds of March, but these effects do not appear to be long-lasting and the plants usually recover for the next season. Mild wet winters can also cause problems by encouraging the leafspot diseases (see page 159) which thrive and are very difficult to control during such weather since sprays are washed off by the rain.

Of the fifteen species I have recognised in the book I would say that the following are definitely rather tender:-

    H. lividus

    H. vesicarius

    H. multifidus, especially plants from southern Italy (subsp. *bocconei*)

    H. thibetanus, hardiness should be in doubt until proven.

    H. cyclophyllus, flowers damaged by hard frosts

My own experience, based on a rather cold Surrey garden, is that *H. lividus* hardly ever survives a winter and even if it does, looks rather unsightly. *H. vesicarius* does survive but is much better if grown in a cold greenhouse. *H. multifidus* is never killed outright but the flowers and their stems are often blackened by frost. *H. cyclophyllus* can be similarly damaged. *H. thibetanus* is an unknown, but plants from the lower altitudes of its range might well be tender. All the rest I regard as completely hardy, although I imagine that those taller species with woody stems, *H. argutifolius* and *H. foetidus*, would be rather vulnerable in winter in some of the colder states of America and Canada.

Siting and Plant Associations. As mentioned above, most Hellebores prefer partial shade with dappled sunlight in the early part of the year such as is provided by deciduous trees and shrubs. However *H. argutifolius* will take more sun and is perfectly happy if planted out in a sunny border, even against a warm wall, which is not surprising since it often occurs in open situations in Corsica. Conversely, it seems to be equally at home in a shady border at Kew on the north side of a wall with a collection of winter flowering plants. I have commented on the tender nature of *H. lividus* so if this is to be attempted in the open garden it requires a sheltered sunny situation, protected from cold winds by a wall or evergreen shrub. *H. vesicarius* is quite different from all other Hellebores in that it makes its growth through late autumn and winter, flowers in the spring, and then dies down during a warm dry summer. It does well in a cold frame with a collection of autumn-winter-spring bulbs, which also have a dormant period in the summer months, but I have also grown it successfully outdoors planted on the sunny side of an evergreen shrub where it received protection in winter and became relatively dry in summer; however it was reluctant to flower under these conditions. It can also be very successfully grown in a large deep pot in a frost-free greenhouse but in this case should not be dried too thoroughly in summer or the roots may dessicate; it must be remembered that in the wild the roots delve down to considerable depths and are almost certainly always in contact with a little moisture even if the surface layers are sunbaked.

H. multifidus is another species which seems to appreciate a more open situation, slightly sheltered to avoid any cold scorching winds in the spring when the soft young growth is emerging.

Apart from these exceptions, all the others are best given partially shaded sites and are ideal subjects for a woodland garden or semi-shaded perennial border where they associate excellently with Snowdrops (*Galanthus*), Winter Aconite (*Eranthis*), early Crocus such as the *C. vernus* and *C. tommasinianus* varieties, and Pulmonarias, to make a great show in the first few months of the year. It is well worth siting some clumps of Hellebores near the house where they can be seen at a time when there is little else and one is not encouraged to go out into the garden. In a woodland setting they are very much at home planted in the open spaces between Rhododendrons or beneath and around deciduous shrubs. One of the joys of gardening is to experiment with plant associations so that the appearance of all the plants involved is enhanced. The possibilities are enormous of course, but a few suggestions for successful relationships are given below:

> Purple or pink *Helleborus orientalis* varieties with white-flowered *Pulmonaria*
> White-flowered *Helleborus orientalis* with blue or pinkish *Pulmonaria*
> Coloured *Helleborus orientalis* varieties with Snowdrops
> White *Helleborus orientalis* planted beneath yellow Forsythia
> *Helleborus foetidus* with red stems of *Cornus alba* 'Sibirica'
> *Arum italicum* 'Pictum' ('Marmoratum') foliage as a foil for *Helleborus orientalis* white, cream and yellow forms
> Early *Narcissus* such as the Cyclamineus Hybrids ('February Gold', 'Tête-à-Tête', 'Dove Wings' etc.) planted between clumps of *H. orientalis* forms
> *H. argutifolius* (*H. corsicus*) is enhanced by silvery foliage such as is provided by Lavender bushes, some *Cistus* species, *Helichrysum angustifolium* etc., in a sunny border
> *Daphne mezereum* associates well with deep coloured *H. orientalis* varieties, or white, to create an early spring display.

Planting and Aftercare. On the whole I would recommend early spring as the best time for moving and planting Hellebores since they are about to make their maximum amount of growth and, in a normal spring, should receive enough rainfall to get them established before the summer. Some growers have advised early autumn as the best time, with the explanation that the plants have a long period in which to settle down before any warm dry summer weather; one could counter this by saying that being disturbed in autumn might make them vulnerable to severe winter weather. Young plants grown in pots can be planted out at almost any time but, if moved in summer, one must be prepared to water them regularly until the roots have become active in their new environment.

The rhizomes of Hellebores should be set just below the soil surface with the growing points level with, or with their tips slightly above, the surface. If buried deeply they do not usually flower well and if too high out of the soil the rhizomes dry out and can be killed. After a few years the rhizomes may work to the surface, or the soil washes away and exposes them, so it is a good idea to top dress with leafmould, old mushroom compost or any well-rotted humus but definitely not fresh manure, since this will encourage too much leaf growth, possibly at the expense of flowers. A light top dressing each year in autumn or spring helps to maintain vigour, keeps the rhizomes covered and helps to retain moisture during dry spells in summer. On poor soils a dressing of general purpose fertilizer in autumn and spring is beneficial, at about the rate of 3 oz per square yard, but one need not be very precise and a light sprinkling around each plant is accurate enough. Choose one of the well balanced (N:P:K) ones, such as National Growmore or bonemeal, or one which is recommended for flower borders.

Whether or not the old leaves are trimmed off in winter or early spring just before flowering time is a matter of personal preference. If the leaves of the *H. orientalis* varieties are healthy and free from blackspot, then they can be left, but I find that so often they look very unsightly by the time the flowers open that they are really best removed and burned. I am sure that removing them, providing it is some time from autumn through to spring, has no ill-effects on the plants.

The stemmed species (*H. argutifolius*, *H. lividus* and *H. foetidus*) require slightly different treatment from the rest. After flowering and seeding the old stems naturally die away and are replaced by new ones which will carry the flowers in the next season. To tidy up the plants, and perhaps divert all the nutrients to the developing young stems, I always cut off the old stems as soon as I have finished with them, either after seeding or after flowering if I do not want the seeds. They can be taken off at ground level and preferably burned in case they are carrying disease spores.

Old clumps of the stemless Hellebores, particularly the *H. orientalis* hybrids, can begin to 'go back' after a few years, losing vigour and becoming sparsely flowered. These can sometimes be rejuvenated by lifting them and dividing them down to single crowns (see chapter on Propagation). The divisions may take a couple of years to settle in and start to flower freely but this is worth trying with old plants which have lost their vigour.

The Christmas Rose, *H. niger*, often flowers very early in the year during the worst of the weather and its pure white blooms can become splashed with mud which in turn may well lead to disease. Cloches placed over the plants may look unsightly in the garden, but they do help to preserve the appearance of this lovely plant and encourage longer stems.

Hellebores as cut flowers. *H. niger* is very successful as a cut flower if one is lucky enough to have a supply, and if they are on good long stems. It lasts well in water whereas most, if not all, of the others tend to wilt rather rapidly. *H. niger* has passed this on to *H. × nigercors* which is a very good cut flower. It is easy to pick the small three-flowered side shoots. I have had some success with the *H. orientalis* varieties by putting the stems into a vase, then cutting off another inch or so of stem whilst under water. Splitting the stems at the base into several strips for at least 2 inches works quite well and the flowers last for about a week. Dipping the tips of the stems into boiling water for 1–2 minutes also seems to lengthen the life of the cut flowers, although I have no idea why it should! A most attractive way of showing Hellebores is to pick individual flowers and float them in a shallow bowl. This way they last for several days, and they face upwards so that their attractive interior colours can be seen. I have noticed that some of the *orientalis* hybrids last as cut flowers much better than others, so possibly there is scope for breeding such a race, for they would be a most attractive commercial proposition.

9

Propagation

There are two methods of propagation of Hellebores: by seed and by division of the rhizomes. The former method has the advantage that a large number of young plants can be raised from one parent, since there may be 50 or more seeds produced by one flower, but on the other hand there is the possibility that the seedlings will not be identical with the parent, either through natural variation or by hybridisation. This may be desirable, but if one is trying to maintain a collection of species Hellebores then it is not welcome and steps must be taken (see below) to prevent cross-pollination by bees which are the main agents involved. Propagation by division has the attraction that all the resulting plants are identical with the parent, that is they represent a clone. If a particular form has been selected, such as a named hybrid cultivar, then this is really the only method which will guarantee young plants which are true to name. The disadvantage is that it is a fairly slow process to build up a stock from one original plant, since each division takes at least a year to settle down and start to perform well. We will now look more closely at these two means of propagation.

Propagation by seed

As mentioned above, the attraction of increasing Hellebores by seed is that it results in a large number of strong young plants. Bees are the main pollinating agents and in most years these are active during any reasonably warm sunny weather when the plants are in flower, even as early as February. Although the pollen is comparatively large and heavy, compared with that of wind-pollinated plants, I am sure that self-pollination also occurs in Hellebores. The stamens are held in very close proximity to the stigmas and it does not take much disturbance of the flower to cause pollen to bridge the small gap. Thus, under normal conditions, seeds are produced quite freely by Hellebores without the need for artificial pollination but to be certain of success it is a good idea to give nature a helping hand. It is unimportant how you transfer pollen from one flower to another. I personally prefer using the black cap of a ball-point pen, rubbed on the trousers to create a little static electricity which causes the pollen to stick on; the pollen is clearly visible against the black plastic and is easily rubbed off on to the stigmas of another plant. The plastic pen cap is very easy to wipe clean before moving on to another species, whereas when using a brush one can never be sure that all the pollen has been removed from between the hairs. Since the stigmas and stamens reach maturity at slightly different times it is worth repeating the process twice or more during the flowering period. If fertilization has been achieved the carpels will begin to swell, whereas unsuccessful attempts are apparent soon after flowering in the form of shrivelled carpels.

If cross-pollination by bees is not desirable, for example if some controlled crosses are to be made, or if a collection of true species is being maintained, then some steps must be taken to prevent access to the flowers by flying insects. Some people merely trim off the perianth segments so that bees have nothing on which to alight, or indeed little to attract them in the first place, but this does not necessarily guarantee isolation and may lead in any case to abortion of the seeds; this is because the perianth segments turn green after flowering and assist in the process of photosynthesis, albeit in a rather small way. Stamens should also be trimmed off to prevent self-pollination if this is considered undesirable for the particular experiment which is to be carried out, for example a hybridisation programme. Isolation of the plant is the safest way of avoiding unwanted cross-pollination and this may be achieved by making a wire frame of fine-mesh netting, such as net curtain material, or by growing the plants in pots and keeping them in an insect-free greenhouse. The latter method has the advantage that the plants are readily accessible and the environment can be controlled to some extent. As most gardeners know, in really inclement winter-spring weather plants will often not produce seeds, even if artificially pollinated, since the temperatures may be too low for proper development.

Hellebores ripen their seeds in late spring or early summer, usually in May or June, and care must be taken at this stage not to lose them all, since the pods (follicles) split open and release their seeds rather suddenly once they are mature. The best way, I find, is to cut off the flower stems just before the pods are ripe and hang them upside down in a paper bag to allow them to dry out and shed the seeds; the pods are usually a pale yellow colour just before they open and if squeezed will begin to split, indicating that they are ready for collection.

For a high percentage germination in the same year it is undoubtedly best to sow immediately, or within a few weeks of collection; germination then occurs in the following autumn or winter. If the seeds cannot be sown straight away it is preferable to store them in polythene bags rather than dry envelopes, and a little slightly dampened moss peat will help to maintain them in good condition. Sowing can then take place at any time during summer or autumn but if delayed too long then germination may well not occur until the following autumn/winter. Dried seed obtained through seed lists is often rather disappointing, either not germinating at all, or at best very spasmodically over several years. A cold period does appear to assist germination and normally I would expect to see seedlings appearing after the first few frosts of autumn.

The technique I employ for sowing is completely traditional, using a proprietary brand of loam-based seed compost in plastic pots. The seeds are sown directly on to this and covered by a good layer of coarse grit which helps to discourage liverworts. The pots are then stood outside and kept watered through the summer. Once germination has occurred they are moved under cover into a cold frame or greenhouse until early spring, by which time the seedlings should be showing the first true leaf and can be handled easily, either to be potted individually and returned to the cold frame or planted out directly into the open ground. In the latter case the seedlings have the opportunity to grow on unchecked but in the early stages are vulnerable to careless weeding and to slugs. Those which are grown on in pots may be planted out at any time whenever they look strong enough.

The time taken to produce flowers varies very much according to the cultural conditions. If grown in fairly rich soil, kept well-watered through the summer and periodically given a dressing of general purpose fertilizer, it is possible to have a flower stem in the first spring after germination, that is in just under one year. However, under normal circumstances at least two complete growing seasons are required for most of the species and hybrids. If the aim of growing from seed is to produce and select hybrids it is best to retain them for more than one flowering season since the first flowers produced may well not exhibit their maximum potential in colour and form.

Propagation by division

Division of rhizomes represents the only practical method of vegetative propagation of Hellebores since to date micropropagation techniques seem to have been rather unsuccessful. I have also tried root cuttings but these were, not surprisingly, a complete failure since there appear to be no latent buds present on the roots, although this does not in itself necessarily mean that pieces of root will never form aerial shoots (take, for example, the case of *Primula denticulata*). Pieces of rhizome without roots attached are very reluctant to produce new roots or shoots so this too is a rather unrewarding exercise.

However, an established Hellebore plant develops a congested rhizome with a mass of fibrous roots and often many growing points, so this does present us with a feasible means of vegetative propagation. On a small scale it is sufficient to take a trowel or spade and cut off a piece of rhizome with shoot and roots attached, leaving the parent plant fairly undisturbed. If a greater number of divisions are required it is preferable to lift the whole clump and tease the various portions apart, using a sharp knife to cut through the tough rhizomes. Each piece should have shoots and roots attached, preferably pale brown (young) roots as well as the older black ones. By this method it is possible to split a clump down to individual crowns resulting in as many as ten or more new plants, all identical to the parent — the attraction of this method of propagation. I personally prefer to do this in early spring before the new leaves begin to grow, during or just after the peak of flowering. The flower stems are removed completely for the operation and if the plant is sizeable I usually turn the hosepipe on it to remove all the soil, thus giving a clear view of the tangled roots and rhizomes. E.B. Anderson (1957), whose opinions on these matters are of great value, recommends late summer or early autumn (August) for the best results, giving the view that the divisions have the opportunity to become established before the winter and well before any dry weather the following summer. Certainly if division is carried out in spring, the young plants need careful attention during any dry weather which follows, and may well not survive prolonged drought. On the other hand, young plants resulting from division in autumn may not tolerate a severe winter, so there are pros and cons to be weighed up before deciding on which particular season to choose.

Having split up a mature plant the resulting divisions can either be planted out into the open ground and left to re-establish or they can be potted and kept in a cold frame for a while until well-rooted enough to be planted out. As with seedling plants it may take at least two years for them to achieve flowering size.

For a nurseryman this method of propagation is too slow and it is to be hoped that micropropagation methods will become possible in due course so that particularly fine hybrids can be made available to a wider public.

10

Hellebore troubles

As a preliminary to dealing with the various problems which arise in growing a collection of Hellebores it should be said that first and foremost it is essential to get the cultivation methods correct in order to obtain a vigorous plant which is capable of recovering from an attack of disease or pest, if not withstanding it altogether.

On the whole there are very few pest problems and of these perhaps greenfly are the worst since they can build up into enormous colonies on the old flowers and undersides of the newly developing leaves in spring and early summer. This causes loss of vigour, and sometimes also distortion of the leaves, and the plants become covered with a sticky mess of honeydew. Probably several species of aphid are involved but *Macrosiphum hellebori*, a relative of the Rose Aphid, is certainly one of them. There are plenty of sprays on the market for dealing with these widespread pests but if you have an aversion to chemicals then, on a small scale, greenfly can be dealt with by rubbing them off the leaves with the thumb, and the old flower stems plus flowers can be cut off and burned if seeds are not required.

Slugs and snails can be a nuisance in the early part of the year when the young buds are just emerging from the soil, and again when the flowers are just beginning to open. In the latter case they often get right into the flower and eat off all the nectaries and stamens. Again, there are plenty of brands of slug pellets and liquid killers available. These I avoid using in spring and summer since we have a lot of visiting hedgehogs which may be harmed if they eat slugs which are dying of metaldehyde poisoning but in winter this does not matter so much since the hedgehogs are, or should be, in hibernation. I usually have an all-out attack on the slugs and snails during the winter using weather-resistant pellets and by catching them under pieces of paving stone or grapefruit halves placed near the plants; they accumulate during the day under such objects and can be despatched by whatever means you can bring yourself to devise!

Other, less troublesome pests which have been recorded include the Leaf Miner, *Phytomyza hellebori*, which disfigures the leaves (noted on *H. niger*), the Garden Swift Moth *Hepialus lupulinus*, whose larvae eat roots, and the Sawfly *Monophadnus longicornis* which can cause galls on stems and leaves.

Diseases can be more serious and are on the whole less easily controlled than pests. The worst problems occur in damp winter and spring weather and involve various leaf spot diseases, of which *Coniothyrium hellebori* is perhaps the worst. Others include *Phyllosticta*, *Ascochyta*, *Ramularia* and *Septoria* species, whilst *Cladosporium herbarum* causes black rot of the leaves. The symptoms are obvious, with black or brown spots and blotches spreading to form rotting areas on the leaves, stems and flowers, sometimes destroying all the stem tissues so that flowers fall off, or keel over. A regular fungicide spraying programme is the only real answer, repeated every 3–4 weeks in winter and spring, and preferably started as soon as the crowns begin to show any signs of pushing into growth; this may entail starting in late autumn and continuing through until after flowering when the new leaves are fairly well expanded. These diseases are far less prevalent in dry winters and I have controlled black spot on one particularly susceptible plant by merely covering it with an open-ended cloche so that the flowers and foliage are never allowed to become wet. It is possible to remove the infected parts and burn them to get some measure of control but this should really be combined with a spraying programme. There is actually no harm in trimming off all the old leaves in autumn so that there is nowhere for the disease to over-winter. I normally do this, but even so I continue to spray the crowns as the buds emerge. Of course with those species which have leafy flower stems in winter, such as *H. argutifolius*, *H. lividus* and *H. foetidus*, this is not possible, but these species do not appear to suffer from leaf-spot to quite the same extent as the stemless species and their hybrids. It does seem to me that some Hellebores are more susceptible than others and I have particular trouble with *H. niger*, *H. multifidus*, *H. cyclophyllus* and *H. purpurascens*. Possibly the reason is that these are less strong-growing in my garden anyway, and therefore less resistant than the more robust ones, rather than possessing some in-built natural resistance to disease.

I have used a variety of different fungicides (e.g. Captan, Dithane) with roughly equal success. The systemic ones based on benomyl are particularly effective and, being systemic, are less affected by heavy rain storms. Non systemic ones can be washed off and I always try to spray again as soon as possible after rain rather than wait for the next routine spray. E.B. Anderson recommended Bordeaux Mixture, which I have not tried out. It is probably worth varying the spray every now and again to discourage any build-up of resistance on the part of the diseases.

Another nasty disease which has been recorded on several species of Hellebore is the smut fungus *Urocystis floccosa* which causes swellings on stems at first, these later bursting open to release a mass of black spores.

Also recorded on Hellebores are various downy mildew fungi such as *Peronospora pulveracea*, *P. hellebori* and *Plasmopara pygmaea*, and the rust fungi *Puccinia acteae-elymi* and *P. acteae-agropyri*, but I have no experience of these and would suggest that they do not constitute serious threats to the health of Hellebores. However it is always worth keeping a close watch on the plants, particularly if a large collection is being grown, and if any unusual symptoms are noted then some specimens should be sent for identification to the Royal Horticultural Society's garden at Wisley, to the Royal Botanic Gardens, Kew, or to the Ministry of Agriculture's Plant Pathology Laboratory at Harpenden.

As a final word on 'troubles' I should add that sometimes Hellebores are damaged by frost to the extent that the flower stems wilt and do not recover, but this need not be a cause for alarm since the leafy shoots should develop slightly later on and will be unharmed. Curiously it is not always during the very severe winters when this happens but sometimes, as in 1988, following a mild winter when there is a sudden late frost. In March 1988 several plants in full flower were ruined by a frost of only $-5°C$ whereas during previous much worse winters the same plants had been subjected to $-12°C$ and their flower stems recovered on thawing out. The vagaries of the British climate must be extremely trying for plants which normally receive a more stable continental type of weather pattern!

Appendices

List of Hellebore Cultivars

The following cultivar names are gleaned primarily from literature, and from such nursery catalogues as have been available to me. The dates of these sources cannot be taken as an accurate statement as to when the plant was first named, and almost certainly many of them were 'christened' earlier than the date shown. Similarly, the authors of the names, especially the 19th century ones, are sometimes only informed guesses since, in the early days, Hellebores were passed from one grower to another and the original raiser was not recorded. Many of the sources given are dated catalogues.

With such fleeting descriptions the value of such a list is fairly low, but may prove useful to those who encounter unknown names in literature, and it also serves to illustrate the wide range which has been available at different times. It may also help to prevent duplication of cultivar names in the future.

The majority of cultivars are 'orientalis hybrids' with tough overwintering leaves. However a few belong to the deciduous types and some to other hybrid groups such as *H. argutifolius* × *H. lividus*, *H. argutifolius* × *H. niger* and *H. lividus* × *H. niger*.

'Abchasicus Albus' (?Berlin 1880s): White tinged green.

'Abchasicus Ruber' (Barr & Sugden 1879): Deep purple.

'Abel Carrière' (Perry cat. ?1930s) uniform crimson-plum, lined crimson.

'Aeneas' (E. Strangman 1980s): A double *H. torquatus*, predominantly green, shaded brown outside.

'Afghan Prince' (Barr Cat. 1899): Deep slaty purple.

'Agnes Brook' (E. Raithby/Court Farm 1988): Pale pink, faintly speckled at base.

'Alabaster' (Washfield Nursery 1971) = nigercors 'Alabaster' (*H. niger* × *H. argutifolius*).

'Alberich' (E. Strangman, 1980s) small blackish-purple, crimson eye.

'Albido-Virescens' (Berlin? 1870s): White flowers tinged green.

'Albin Otto' (or 'Olban Otto') (Heinemann, before 1884): white, spotted purple.

'Aldebaran' (E. Smith c. 1970): Early flowering, bright red-purple, golden nectaries. 'H. atrorubens hort.' seedling.

'Amethyst' (H. Ballard 1986 cat.): Bluish mauve, yellow nectaries.

'Anderson's Red Hybrids' (E.B. Anderson c. 1950s) Variable reddish-plum.

'Andromeda' (E. Smith c. 1970): Blackish-purple with bluish bloom

'Antares' (E. Smith c. 1970): Red-purple

'Apotheker Bogren' (Heinemann 1880s): Large pale rosy purple, profusely crimson spotted.

'Aquarius' (E. Smith c. 1970): Rose pink with small crimson speckles

'Aquila' (J. Archibald 1978): white with crimson base and nectaries

'Archer Hind' (Perry cat. ?1930s) pink shaded dark rose, faintly spotted.

'Ariel' (E. Smith c. 1967): *H. torquatus* hybrid, pale green, speckled crimson inside; purple outside.

'Arthur Collins' (Barr 1881): Reddish purple, profusely spotted inside.

'Atroroseus' (Barr 1879, probably ex Berlin): Pale rosy purple, tipped green.

'Atrorubens' ('atrorubens of gardens') = A form of *H. orientalis* subsp. *abchasicus*, now called 'Early Purple'.

'Ballard's Black' (E. Ballard 1920s): Large blackish-purple, overlapping sepals.

'Banana Split' (Henry A. Ross, Ohio, 1984): Large yellowish-cream.

'Beatrix' (E.B. Anderson, 1967): A × *nigercors* form.

'Belinda' (E. Strangman 1987) Small double pink. 'Dido' seedling.

'Bismark' (Barr cat. 1893): Deep plum purple.

'Black Knight' (Barr A.M. 1926, prob. German origin): Deep purple-black.

'Blowsy' (H. Ballard 1988 cat.): Large cream.

'Blue Spray' (H. Ballard 1988 cat.): Medium sized, bluish.

'Blue Wisp' (H. Ballard 1983 cat.): Tall, with small dark bluish flowers.

'Boughton Beauty' (V. Finnis ?1970s): A × *sternii* selection.

'Bowles' Yellow' (named by G.S. Thomas, possibly ex Glasnevin): Pale yellow.

'Bridesmaid' (Henry A. Ross, Ohio, 1984): White spotted pink in centre.

'Brünhilde' (?pre 1880): Vigorous, cream.

'Brutus' (Barr. cat. 1893): Deep plum purple.

'Burgundy' (H. Ballard 1986 cat.): Deep purple, good shape.

'Button' (H. Ballard 1983 cat.): Neat globular ivory flowers.

'Capricornus' (E. Smith c. 1970):

'Carina' (J. Archibald 1978): Pink veined, darker crimson basal stain; bronze nectaries.

'Carlton Hall' (E. Raithby/Court Farm 1988): Large white spotted purple.

'Cassiopeia' (E. Smith c.1970) Shell-pink, tinged green.

'Castor' (E. Smith c. 1967): Black-purple.

'Caucasicus Lutescens' (Barr cat. 1899): Rich clear creamy yellow.

'Celadon' (E. Strangman 1980s) Clear mid-green.

'Chancellor' (Barr cat. 1899): Clear rose.

'Cheerful' (H. Ballard 1988 cat.): Clear pale yellow.

'Citron' (H. Ballard 1983 cat.): Clear pale yellow (Mimosa yellow 602/1).

'Colchicus Coccineus' (Barr cat. 1889): Rich plum.

'Colchicus Punctatus' (Barr & Sugden cat. 1879): Deep purple spotted all over.

'Columbine' (Barr. cat. 1880s): Deciduous, purple outside, green inside.

'Commandant Benary' (Perry cat ?1930s) Pure white, fluted pea-green, spotted crimson.

'Commerzienrath Benary' (Heinemann 1870s): Green-white, spotted purple.

'Coombe Fishacre Purple' (Archer-Hind 1870s): Rosy purple.

'Coombe Fishacre Yellow' (Archer-Hind 1870s): Pale yellow-green.

'Corvus' (J. Archibald c. 1980): Black-maroon, bronze nectaries.

'Cosmos' (E. Smith c. 1973): Pale pink, densely speckled crimson, vigorous.

'Cream Strain' (E. Smith 1968): Creamy white flushed green.

'Darley Mill' (E. Raithby/Court Farm 1988): Pale pink spotted burgundy.

'Dawn' (H. Ballard 1988): Large pink.

'December Dawn' (H. Ballard 1987): A *niger* × *lividus* cross.

'Desdemona' (Perry cat. ?1930s) soft pink.

'Dick Crandon' (H. Ballard 1985): Clear pale pink.

'Dido' (E. Strangman 1980s): A double *H. torquatus*, green inside, purple outside.

'Dora Froebel' (Perry cat. ?1930s).

'Dotty' (H. Ballard 1986 cat.): Pink, heavily spotted purple.

'Dowager' (Henry A. Ross, Ohio, 1984): Large deep rose pink.

'Dr. Hogg' (Barr cat. 1899): Rich deep rose.

'Dr. Moore' (Glasnevin, late 19th c.): Pink outside, paler & unspotted inside.

'Draco' (E. Smith c. 1970): Pink outside, crimson with pale rose edge inside.

'Dusk' (H. Ballard 1985): Large purple with blue 'bloom' inside.

'Early Purple' (B. Mathew 1988): A cv. name for "H. atrorubens of gardens".

'Electra' (E. Smith c. 1970): 'Atrorubens hort' × *torquatus*. wine purple with blue bloom.

'Elegans' (or *guttatus* 'Elegans') (Barr & Sugden cat. 1881): White spotted purple.

'Elizabeth Coburn' (Court Farm 1988): Old rose, overlaid burgundy.

'Elizabeth Rose' (Perry cat. ?1930s): Soft rose shaded white, heavily spotted maroon.

'Ellen Terry' (Barr. cat. 1897); Pinkish-purple suffused green, finely spotted inside.

'Ena' (Duchess of Bedford A.M. 1920): Dark maroon.

'Ernest Raithby' (E. Raithby/Court Farm 1988): Light purple.

'Erubescens' (T. Moore, Gard. Chron. 1879): Deciduous, yellow-green flushed pink.

'F.C. Heinemann' (Heinemann 1880s): Pale purple outside, pale green spotted purple inside.

'First Kiss' (Henry A. Ross, Ohio, 1984): Light blush pink.

foetidus 'Italian Form': A very floriferous form.

foetidus 'Miss Jekyll's Scented Form': Daphne-scented.

foetidus 'Wester Flisk' (c. 1984): Stems reddish-purple, leaves lead-green.

'Frau Irene Heinemann' (Heinemann 1870s): Purple with darker veins & spots.

'Fred Whitsey' (Court Farm 1988): White with maroon blotches.

'Friar Tuck' (Perry cat. ?1930s): rosy crimson flushed white, heavy maroon spotting.

'Frühlingfreude' (H. Klose 1978): Pink with crimson spotting.

'Fulvus' (Barr & Sugden 1879): Red-purple suffused coppery-brown.

'Galaxy Strain' (E. Smith 1960): Blush-white tinged green, speckled maroon, variable.

'Garnet' (H. Ballard 1988): Brownish-red.

'Gaston Dugourd' (see *Revue Horticole* 1902): Pink blotched crimson (said to be *foetidus* × *purpurascens* × *niger*!).

'Gemini' (E. Smith c. 1970): Pink with maroon spots.

'Gertie' (Duchess of Bedford A.M. 1920): Light claret, spotted darker.

'Gertrude Froebel' (Perry cat. ?1930s) soft rose, pea-green outside.

'Gertrude Jekyll' (Barr cat. 1889): Cream-white, spotted red.

'Gertrude Raithby' (E. Raithby/Court Farm 1988): Pale pink spotted burgundy.

'Greencups' (H. Ballard 1985): Mid-green, very vigorous.

'Greenland' (Margery Fish 1960s): White tinged green, variable.

'Gremlin' (Henry A. Ross, Ohio, 1984): Yellowish-green.

'Gretchen Heinemann' (Heinemann 1880s): Rosy purple, many crimson spots.

'Guttatus Leichtlinii' (Barr cat. 1889): Creamy white, spotted red.

'Guttatus Subpunctatus' (Barr cat. 1889): Creamy white with few spots.

'Hades' (H. Ballard 1988): Slate blue, stippled.

'Hawkhurst' (Davenport-Jones 1950s): A × *nigercors* selection.

'Hazy Dawn'.

'Heartsease' (Bloom ?1970s): variable maroon.

'Hecate' (H. Ballard 1985): Dark purple, stippled.

'Helen Ballard' (H. Ballard 1987): Vivid green.

'Helena' (J. Archibald 1981): white speckled at base, vigorous.

'Henri Dugourd' (see *Revue Horticole* 1902): reputedly (*foetidus* × *purpurascens* × *niger*!)

'Hercules' (E. Smith c. 1970): Rose purple outside, spotted crimson inside.

'Hidcote Double' (G.S. Thomas 1987 ex Hidcote Manor): Double purple.

'Highbury Hybrids' (S. Cherry).

'Hilliers' White' (Hillier & Sons 1960s): White.

'Hofgarten—Inspektor Hartwig' (Heinemann 1880s): Rosy purple flushed green, spotted crimson.

'Hyades' (E. Smith c. 1970): Greenish white, cream heavily spotted crimson inside).

'Ian Raithby' (E. Raithby/Court Farm 1988): Wine red with netted pattern inside.

'Inca' (J. Archibald 1981): Slate purple.

'Indigo' (H. Ballard 1983): Dark purple-blue, plant short.

'Ingot' (H. Ballard 1983): Yellow (Aureolin 3/1).

'James Atkins' (Barr cat. 1893): Rosy purple.

'John Cross' (E. Raithby/Court Farm 1988): Deep ruby red.

'John Raithby' (E. Raithby/Court Farm 1988): Old rose, overlaid magenta.

'Kamtschatensis' (continental origin, 19th c): Pink with dark wine netting.

'Lady Leonora' (Barr cat. 1899): Rose pink, silvery rose inside.

'Leichtlinii' (Leichtlin, ?1870s): Cream-white, spotted red.

'Leo' (E. Smith c. 1970): Rose pink with zone of crimson spots.

'Libra' (E. Smith c. 1970): Pale pink with maroon-purple spots.

'Lime Ice' (Henry A. Ross, Ohio, 1984): White outside, lime green inside.

'Little Black' (E. Strangman 1970s) 'Pluto' hybrid.

'Little Stripey' (E. Strangman 1980s): A *H. torquatus* selection, dark violet outside, green striped violet inside.

'Lividescens' (Barr cat. 1889, prob. continental origin): Dull purple tinged green.

'Lividescens Pallidus' (Barr cat. 1899): Creamy yellow.

'Longstock' (Longstock Park Gardens).

'Luridus' (Barr cat. 1889): ? a *H. torquatus* form; green inside, brown-purple outside; foliage much-divided.

'Luteus Grandiflorus' (Glasnevin 1880s): Pale lemon yellow.

'Lynne' (H. Ballard 1988): White, faintly speckled.

'Maiden's Blush' (Perry cat. ?1930s): rosy white flushed deep red at edges.

'Mardi Gras' (Henry A. Ross, Ohio, 1984): White with deep red blotch in centre.

'Margaret Mathew' (B. Mathew 1967): White, wavy-edged, finely speckled maroon.

'Mars' (E. Smith 1960): Red purple.

'Mary Petit' (E. Raithby/Court Farm 1988): Cream, lightly speckled at base.

'Mercury' (E. Smith, c. 1960): white with few basal crimson dots.

'Midnight Sky Strain' (E. Smith 1970): Rich purple with glaucous 'bloom', speckled darker.

'Midwinter' (H. Ballard 1973): A *niger* × *lividus* selection.

'Ministre Jean Dupuy' (see Revue Horticole 1902): Deep rose, blotched crimson in centre (reputedly *foetidus* × *purpurascens* × *niger*!).

'Mira' (E. Smith c. 1970): Near to 'Cosmos'; pink flecked crimson, cup-shaped.

'Miranda' (E. Smith 1974): A *H. torquatus* hybrid, vinous outside, paler & speckled inside.

'Nancy Ballard' (H. Ballard 1986): White, faintly speckled pink.

'Neptune' (E. Smith c. 1970): Slate purple *H. torquatus* cross.

niger 'Allerseelen'

niger 'Altifolius'

niger 'Apple Blossom' (= 'Ruber') (Barr cat. 1893): Rosy white, darker outside.

niger 'Brockhurst' (W. Brockbank 19th c.): = 'St. Brigid'.

niger 'Caucasicus' (Barr cat. 1889): White tinged rose, fragrant.

niger 'De Graaff's Var' (?19th c.): Flowers pale primrose with age.

niger 'Flore Roseo' (Gard. Chron. 1888): Pink.

niger 'Foliis Variegatis' (Barr cat. 1889): Young leaves variegated.

niger 'Grandiflorus'

niger 'Juvernis' (Barr cat. 1893): = 'St Brigid'.

niger 'Ladham's Variety' (early 20th c.?): Similar to 'Potters Wheel'.

niger 'Louis Cobbett' (L. Cobbett, 1950s?): Strong pink suffusion.

niger 'Madame Fourcade' (Barr cat. 1889): Pure white.

niger 'Major' (Barr cat. 1889): Very large flowers.

niger 'Maximus' (Barr cat. 1889): Very large, rose tinted.

niger 'Minor' (Barr cat. 1889): Small flowers.

niger 'Mr Poë's Variety' (J.B. Poë 1880s):

niger 'Potter's Wheel' (Tristram/ Davenport-Jones? 1950s): Large white with green eye, good shape. AM, 1958.

niger 'Praecox': Early flowering form with large round flowers.

niger 'Riverston' or 'Riverstoni' (J.B. Poë ?1880s): Early, with long stalks, fragrant.

niger 'Rubra' (Barr cat. 1889): Rosy-white, outside purple-red.

niger 'Scoticus' (Barr cat. 1889): White tinged rose.

niger 'St. Brigid' (Burbidge c. 1850): Leaves overtopping the flowers.

niger 'The Bath', or 'Bath Christmas Rose' (Barr cat. 1889): Large, late flowering.

niger 'Trotter's Form' (R. Trotter ?1970s): Large, becoming apricot with age.

niger 'Van Keesen'.

niger 'Vernalis' (Barr cat. 1895): same as 'Caucasicus'.

niger 'Wardie Lodge' (Miss F.J. Hope, late 19th c.): Large, tinged pink.

niger 'White Magic' (A.R. White, ex N. Zealand, 1987): White aging to pink.

× *nigercors* 'Alabaster' (Washfield Nursery 1971): *niger* × *argutifolius*.

× *nigercors* 'Beatrix' (E.B. Anderson 1967): *niger* × *argutifolius*.

× *nigercors* 'Hawkhurst' (Davenport-Jones 1950s): *niger* × *argutifolius*.

'Nigericors' = × *nigercors*.

'Nigricans' (Froebel cat. 1900): Indigo blue-black.

'Nigricors' = *nigercors*.

'Nigristern' (E. Smith 1972): *niger* × (× *sternii*)

'Nocturne' (H. Ballard 1988): Dark, nearly blue.

'Oberon' (E. Smith cat. 1975): *H. torquatus* cross, dark purple outside, green-white inside.

'Odoratus' (cult. by Archer-Hind 1880s): Elder-scented, ?green.

'Odoratus Nanus' (cult. by Archer-Hind 1880s): Elder-scented, ?green.

'Olban Otto' or 'Albin Otto' (Barr cat. 1893): White spotted crimson.

'Old Ugly' (E. Strangman 1960s): green *viridis* hybrid heavily red spotted.

'Olympicus Major' (Barr & Sugden cat. 1880): White tinged green.

'Orion' (J. Archibald 1978): Cream tinged green, purple stain in centre and purple nectaries.

'Otto Froebel' (Froebel 1880s/Barr cat. 1893):

'Pallidus' (Cult. Ellacombe 1877 ex Berlin): White tinged green-yellow.

'Pallidus Albus' (cult. Ellacombe 1877 ex Berlin): Whitish.

'Parrot' (H. Ballard 1987): Golden-green.

'Patchwork' (H. Ballard 1988): Small fl., flushed green & pale blue.

'Paul Mathew' (B. Mathew 1987); White with solid maroon eye.

'Pebworth White' (E. Raithby/Court Farm 1988): White with few maroon spots.

'Pedatus' (T. Archer-Hind 1884): Deciduous, large yellow-green.

'Peggy Ballard' (H. Ballard 1986): Glowing red.

'Peter Rudolph Barr' (Barr cat. 1889, A.M., Barr 1908): Red purple, spotted inside.

'Petsamo' (?): White tinged green with few maroon spots.

'Philip Ballard' (H. Ballard 1986): Very dark blue-black.

'Philip Wilson' (H. Ballard 1986): Clear pink, spotted deeper pink.

'Pink Strain' (E. Smith 1970): Shell pink to soft rose.

'Pleiades' (E. Smith 1967): White, densely speckled dark maroon, dwarf.

'Pluto' (E. Smith 1960): *H. torquatus* hybrid, wine purple outside, green and slaty purple inside. Purple nectaries.

'Polaris' (E. Smith c. 1970): Pure white, vigorous.

'Pollux' (E. Smith c. 1970): Black-purple, weak.

'Porphyromelas' (cult. Ellacombe 1877, ex Berlin).

'Pourpre Royal' (Perry cat. ?1930s): crimson-purple, conspicuous sulphur anthers.

'Primrose' (P. Chappell c. 1970): Pale primrose.

'Primrose Dame' (T. Archer-Hind 1880s): Yellowish-green.

'Prince Rupert' (Barr, A.M. 1927): Creamy-white, densely speckled red.

'Professor Schleicher' (Barr cat. 1889, continental origin): Pure white.

'Psyche' (Barr cat. 1899): Soft pink with crimson blotch in centre.

'Punctatissimus' (Barr cat. 1889): Bright

rose-purple, profusely spotted.

'Punctatus' (Barr & Sugden 1881): Deep purple, spotted inside.

'Punctatus Hybridus' (cult. Ellacombe 1877 ex Berlin):

'Purple Strain' (E. Smith 1968): Dusky plum purple, variable.

'Queen Christina' (Perry cat. ?1930s): soft rose flushed pea-green faintly spotted.

'Queen of the Night' (E. Strangman 1970s): Dark purple with plum bloom. Dark nectaries.

'Queen of the North (?): White with sparse red spots, wavy-edged.

'Red Spur' (F.C. Stern 1935).

'Red Wine Dob' (C. Smith, Australia, 1986): Deep pink with purple blotches merging in centre.

'Rembrandt' (H. Ballard 1988): Dark brown-red.

'Reticulatus' (cult. Ellacombe 1877, ex Berlin).

'Rosa' (H. Ballard 1988): Pink.

'Roseus' (Barr cat. 1889: Deep rose.

'Roseus Punctatus' (Barr cat. 1889): Deep rose, profusely spotted.

'Rossini' (H. Ballard 1988): Clear red.

'Rubellus' (Barr & Sugden 1879): Light rose-pinkish-purple, glaucous.

'Rubens' (H. Ballard 1987): Deep red.

'Ruber' (Barr & Sugden 1879): Reddish-purple, greenish-purple inside.

'Ruberissimus' (Barr cat. 1889): Red-purple.

'Rubidus' (M. Leichtlin 1880s): Reddish-plum, spotted darker.

'Rubro-Purpureus' (Barr & Sugden 1879): Deep reddish-plum.

'Sambuc-odorus' (cult. T. Archer Hind 1880s): Elder scented, ?colour.

'Sarah Ballard' (H. Ballard 1986): Pale clear cream.

'Scorpio' (E. Smith c. 1970): Soft pink, crimson-speckled inside.

'Seagull' (Perry cat. ?1930s): white, faintly flushed pea-green.

'Selene' (J. Archibald 1978): Yellow flushed lime-green, *H. cyclophyllus* × 'Sirius'.

'Sirius' (E. Smith c. 1974): Primrose yellow, flowers held up.

'Snow Sprite' (Perry cat. ?1930s): Snow-white, conspicuous green centre.

'Snowdon' (Perry cat. ?1930s): Snow-white, maroon-crimson spotting.

'Sophia Froebel' (Perry cat. ?1930s): plum-rose, lined maroon.

'Sorcerer' (Henry A. Ross, Ohio, 1984): Dark purple-black, glaucous.

'Southern Belle' (Henry A. Ross, Ohio, 1984): Large lavender.

'Speciosus' (Barr & Sugden cat. 1881): Large white, spotted.

'Spotty Vanda' (C. Smith, Australia, 1986): Green in centre, pink at edges, dark-spotted all over.

'Stella Polaris' (Perry cat. ?1930s): Snow-white, faintly stained green.

'Stephen Olbritch' (T. Lawrence 1898).

× *sternii* 'Blackthorn Strain' (A.R. White 1987): *argutifolius* × *lividus* selection.

× *sternii* 'Boughton Beauty' (V. Finnis 1970s): *argutifolius* × *lividus* selection.

'Sub-punctatus' (?Heinemann 1880s): Cream-white, sparsely spotted.

'Sulphur Gem' (Perry cat. ?1930s): sulphury-white, faintly spotted red.

'Sulphureus' (Barr cat. 1889): Yellow.

'Sunny' (H. Ballard 1988): Creamy yellow.

'Sylvia' (H. Ballard 1985): White.

'Taurus' (E. Smith c. 1972): Pink with zone of large crimson spots inside.

'Thomas S. Ware' (T. Ware 1880s): Unspotted deep rosy purple.

'Titania' (J. Archibald c. 1980): Mushroom pink outside, greenish-cream inside.

'Tom Thumb' (Barr. cat. 1899): Dwarf, rose pink with yellow shading.

'Torquatus Hybrids' (E. Smith 1974): Dwarf, variable purplish shades.

'Trotters Spotted' (R. Trotter, ?1960s):

'Unique' (Perry cat. ?1930s): Rosy-white, spotted light red.

'Upstart' (H. Ballard 1983): Pink with rounded flowers.

'Ushba' (H. Ballard 1983): Pure white, good shape.

'Venus' (E. Smith c. 1962): Greenish-white with basal zone of crimson flecks inside, dwarf.

'Victoria Raithby' (E. Raithby/Court Farm 1988): Pale pink.

'Violetta' (E. Strangman 1986): white, purple picotee, lightly purple spotted.

'W.E. Gladstone' (Barr cat. 1893): Rosy

purple, veined inside.

'Wester Flisk': *H. foetidus* selection with reddish stems.

'White Cap' (Perry cat. ?1930s): Snow-white.

'White Swan' (?): White, green in centre with few red spots.

'Willie Schmidt' (?Heinemann 1880s): Pure white.

'Winter Cheer' (A. Bloom 1970s): Variable seed-raised strain.

'Yellow Button' (H. Ballard 1986): Small deep yellow.

'Zodiac Strain' (E. Smith 1974): Pink with purple spotting.

'Zuleika' (J. Archibald 1982): *H. torquatus* hybrid, large flower red-purple outside, inside green-white flushed red.

APPENDIX B

Finding List of Helleborus names

(For cultivar names see page 163)

Names in **bold italic** refer to species,
subspecies etc that are used as accepted
names in this book. Others represent
synonyms with references to the accepted
names.

abascius Passerini = *orientalis* subsp.
  abchasicus
abchasicus A. Braun = *orientalis* subsp.
  abchasicus
abschasicus A. Braun = *orientalis* subsp.
  abchasicus
albus Gueldenst. = *Veratrum album*
altifolius (Hayne) Reichb. = variant of *H.*
  niger
angustifolius Host = multifidus subsp.
  multifidus
antiquorum A. Braun = orientalis subsp.
  orientalis
argutifolius Viv.
atropurpureus Schultes = *atrorubens*
atrorubens Waldst. & Kit.
  forma **cupreus** (Host) Martinis
  forma **hircii** Martinis
  forma **incisus** Martinis
baumgartenii (Kov.) Schur = *purpurascens*
  forma *baumgartenii*
beugesiacus Jord. & Fourr. = *foetidus*
biflorus Vilmorin = *orientalis* subsp.
  orientalis
bocconei Tenore = *multifidus* subsp.
  bocconei
brevicaulis Fourr. = viridis subsp. viridis
casta-diva Busch subsp. *kochii* (Schiffner)
  Busch = orientalis subsp. orientalis
casta-diva Busch subsp. abchasicus (A.Br.)
  Busch = orientalis subsp. abchasicus
caucasicus A.Br. = *orientalis* subsp.
  orientalis.
caucasicus var. *abchasica* (A.Br.)
  Regel = *orientalis* subsp. *abchasicus*

caucasicus var. *abchasicus* (A.Br.)
  Regel = *orientalis* subsp. *abchasicus*
caucasicus var. *cholchica* Regel = *orientalis*
  subsp. *abchasicus*
caucasicus var. *colchicus* (Regel)
  Regel = *orientalis* subsp. *abchasicus*
caucasicus var. *guttatus* (A.Br. & Sauer)
  Regel = *orientalis* subsp. *guttatus*
caucasicus var. *pallidus* Regel = *orientalis*
  subsp. *orientalis*
chinensis Maxim. = *thibetanus*
colchicus Regel = *orientalis* subsp.
  abchasicus
corsicus Willd. = nomen nudum
corsicus subsp. *corsicus* forma *angustifolius*
  Schiffner = *argutifolius*
corsicus subsp. *corsicus* forma *latifolius*
  Schiffner = *argutifolius*
corsicus subsp. *lividus* (Ait.)
  Schiffner = *lividus*
corsicus subsp. *lividus* forma *angustifolius*
  Schiffner = *lividus*
corsicus subsp. *lividus* forma *latifolius*
  Schiffner = *lividus*
corsicus subsp. *lividus* var. *pictus*
  Schiffner = *lividus*
croaticus Martinis = variant of *torquatus*
croaticus forma *angustisectus*
  Martinis = variant of *torquatus*
croaticus forma *latisectus*
  Martinis = variant of *torquatus*
croaticus forma *polysectus*
  Martinis = variant of *torquatus*
cupreus Host = variant of *atrorubens*
cyclophyllus (A.Br.) Boiss.
decorus Le Bele = *odorus*
deflexifolius Jord. & Fourr. = *foetidus*
× *dives* A.Br. = garden hybrid
  (*purpurascens* × *orientalis* subsp.
  guttatus)

dumetorum Waldst. & Kit.

dumetorum subsp. *atrorubens* (W. & K.)
Merxm. & Podl. = *atrorubens*

dumetorum forma *incisus*
Schiffner = variant of *dumetorum*

dumetorum forma *laciniatus*
Martinis = variant of *dumetorum*

dumetorum forma *majoriflorus*
Borbas = variant of *dumetorum*

dumetorum forma *multisectus*
Schiffner = variant of *dumetorum*

dumetorum forma *pauciflorus*
Schiffner = variant of *dumetorum*

× *fissus* Schiffner = garden hybrid (?
multifidus × *olympicus*)

foetidus Linn.

fumarioides Lam. = *Isopyrum fumarioides*

grandiflorus Koch ex Ruprecht = *orientalis*
subsp. *guttatus*

grandiflorus Salisb. = *niger* subsp.
macranthus

graveolens Host = *odorus*

guttatus A.Br. & Sauer = *orientalis* subsp.
guttatus

hercegovinus Martinis = *multifidus* subsp.
hercegovinus

heterophyllus Wender ex Steud. = ? not a
Helleborus

× *heyderi* Schiffner = garden hybrid
(*orientalis* subsp. *guttatus* × subsp.
abchasicus)

hunfalvyanus Kanitz var. *atrorubens* (W. &
K.) Kanitz = *atrorubens*

hunfalvyanus var. *cupreus* (Host)
Kanitz = *atrorubens*

hunfalvyanus var. *dumetorum* (W. & K.)
Kanitz = *dumetorum*

hunfalvyanus var. *graveolens* (Host)
Kanitz = *odorus*

hunfalvyanus var. *multifidus* (Vis.)
Kanitz = *multifidus* subsp. *multifidus*

hunfalvyanus var. *odorus* (W. & K.)
Kanitz = *odorus*

hunfalvyanus var. *purpurascens* (W. & K.)
Kanitz = *purpurascens*

hunfalvyanus var. *viridis* (L.)
Kanitz = *viridis* subsp. *viridis*

× *hybridus* Voss = general name for garden
hybrids

hyemalis Linn. = *Eranthis hyemalis*

ibericus Stev. ex Rupr. = *orientalis* subsp.
orientalis

intermedius Guss. = *multifidus* subsp.
bocconei

intermedius Hirc = *atrorubens* forma *hircii*

intermedius Host = *torquatus*

intermedius Morren = *orientalis* subsp.
guttatus

involucratus Stokes = *Eranthis hyemalis*

istriacus (Schiffner) Borbas = *multifidus*
subsp. *istriacus*

× *jourdanii* Pagès = natural hybrid
(*foetidus* × *viridis*)

× *kamtschatensis* Ellacombe ex
Schiffner = garden hybrid (*orientalis*
group)

kochii Schiffner = *orientalis* subsp.
orientalis

kochii var. *glaber* Schiffner = *orientalis*
subsp. *orientalis*

kochii var. *hirtus* Schiffner = *orientalis*
subsp. *orientalis*

latifolius Miller = description insufficient
to identify

laxus Host = *multifidus* subsp. *istriacus*

× *lividescens* A.Br. & Sauer = garden
hybrid (*purpurascens* × *orientalis* subsp.
abchasicus)

lividus Aiton in Hortus
Kewensis = *argutifolius*

lividus Aiton in Curtis Bot. Mag.

lividus subsp. *corsicus* (Briq.)
Tutin = invalid

lividus subsp. *corsicus* (Briq.)
Yeo = *argutifolius*

lividus var. *integrifolius* DC. = *lividus*

lividus var. *integrilobus* DC. = *lividus*

× *lucidus* Ellacombe ex Schiffner = garden
hybrid

macranthus (Freyn) Dalla Torre &
Sarnth. = *niger* subsp. *macranthus*

macranthus Koch = *orientalis* subsp.
guttatus

monanthos Moench = *Eranthis hyemalis*

multifidus Vis. subsp. *multifidus*

multifidus subsp. *bocconei* (Tenore) B.
Mathew

multifidus var. *bocconei* (Tenore)
Schiffner = *multifidus* subsp. *bocconei*

multifidus subsp. *hercegovinus* (Martinis)
B. Mathew

multifidus subsp. *istriacus* (Schiffner)
Merxm. & Podl.

multifidus forma *istriacus* (Schiffner)

Martinis = *multifidus* subsp. *istriacus*

multifidus subsp. *laxus* (Host)
Martinis = *multifidus* subsp. *istriacus*

multifidus subsp. *serbicus* (Adam.) Merxm.
& Podl. = *torquatus*

nemoralis Jord. & Fourr. = foetidus

niger Linn. subsp. **niger**

niger subsp. **macranthus** (Freyn) Schiffner

niger var. *altifolius* Hayne = variant of
niger

niger var. *angustifolius* = variant of *niger*

niger var. *humilifolius* Hayne = variant of
niger

niger var. *laciniatus* Gusmus ex
Hegi = variant of *niger*

niger var. *macranthus* Freyn = *niger* subsp.
macranthus

niger var. *oblongifolius* Beck = variant of
niger

niger var. *stenopetalus* Beck = variant of
niger

niger var. *typicus* Beck = *niger* subsp. *niger*

nivalis Siev. ex Ledeb. = *Eranthis*

occidentalis Reuter = *viridis* subsp.
occidentalis

odorus Waldst. & Kit.

odorus subsp. *laxus* (Host) Merxm. &
Podl. = *multifidus* subsp. *istriacus*

odorus subsp. *multifidus* (Vis.)
Hayek = *multifidus* subsp. *multifidus*

odorus subsp. *multifidus* var. *violascens*
(Beck) Hayek = *torquatus*

odorus var. *atrorubens* (W. & K.)
Koch = *atrorubens*

odorus var. *graveolens* (Host)
Maly = *odorus*

odorus var. *istriacus* Schiffner = *multifidus*
subsp. *istriacus*

odorus forma *angustifolius* Beck = variant
of *odorus*

odorus forma *javorkae* Horvat = variant of
odorus

odorus forma *laceratus* K. Maly = variant
of *odorus*

odorus forma *latifolius* Beck = variant of
odorus

odorus forma *mecsekensis*
Horvat = variant of *odorus*

odorus forma *multisectus*
Martinis = variant of *odorus*

odorus forma *parviflorus* Priszter = variant
of *odorus*

odorus forma *purpureiformis*
Horvat = variant of *odorus*

officinalis Salisb. = *orientalis*

officinalis var. *atrorubens* (W. & K.)
Spach = *atrorubens*

olympicus Lindley = *orientalis* subsp.
orientalis

orientalis Lamarck subsp. **orientalis**

orientalis subsp. **abchasicus** (A.Br.) B.
Mathew

orientalis subsp. **guttatus** (A.Br. & Sauer)
B. Mathew

pallidus Host = *dumetorum*

personati Masclef = *viridis* ? subsp.
occidentalis

polychromus A.A. Kolak. = *orientalis*

polychromus var. *guttatus* (A.Br. & Sauer)
Kolak = *orientalis* subsp. *guttatus*

ponticus A.Br. = *orientalis* subsp. *orientalis*

porphyromelas A.Br. &
Bouché = *orientalis* subsp. *abchasicus*

pumilus Salisb. = *Coptis trifolia*

× *punctatus* Nicholson = garden hybrid
(*orientalis* group)

purpurascens Waldst. & Kit.

purpurascens var. *baumgartenii*
Kovats = *purpurascens* forma
baumgartenii

purpurascens var. *subflagellatus*
Schur = *purpurascens* forma
baumgartenii

purpurascens var. *viridiflorus*
Schur = *purpurascens* forma *viridiflorus*

purpurascens forma *asperus*
Simk. = variant of *purpurascens*

purpurascens forma *baumgartenii* (Kov.)
Nyár. = variant of *purpurascens*

purpurascens forma *dniesterensis*
Zapal. = variant of *purpurascens*

purpurascens forma *glabrescens*
Simk. = variant of *purpurascens*

purpurascens forma *grossedentatus*
Nyár. = variant of *purpurascens*

purpurascens forma *nanus* Zapal. = variant
of *purpurascens*

purpurascens forma *quadriflorus*
Zapal. = variant of *purpurascens*

purpurascens forma *subdivisus*
Zapal. = variant of *purpurascens*

purpurascens forma *tuzsonii*
Andréanszky = variant of *purpurascens*

purpurascens forma

typicus = *purpurascens*

purpurascens forma *viridiflorus* (Schur.) Nyár. = variant of *purpurascens*

pyrenaicus Zahlb. ex Schiffner = *viridis* subsp. *occidentalis*

ranunculinus Smith = *Trollius ranunculinus*

rhodanicus Jord. & Fourr. = *foetidus*

serbicus Adamović = *torquatus*

serbicus subsp. *malyi* Martinis = *torquatus*

serbicus forma *gočensis* Gajić = variant of *torquatus*

serbicus forma *latisectus* Gajić = variant of *torquatus*

sibiricus Spreng. = *Eranthis sibiricus*

siculus Schiffner = *multifidus* subsp. *bocconei*

spinescens Tausch ex Schiffner = *argutifolius*

× *sternii* Turrill = garden hybrid (*argutifolius* × *lividus*)

teeta Baill. = *Coptis teeta*

thalictrioides Lam. = *Isopyrum thalictrioides*

thibetanus Franchet

tinctus Stev. ex Rupr. = *orientalis* subsp. *abchasicus*

torquatus Archer Hind

trifoliatus Houtt. = *Coptis trifolia*

trifolius Linn. = *Coptis trifolia*

trifolius Miller = *lividus*

trifolius Miller subsp. *corsicus* Briquet = *argutifolius*

trifolius subsp. *lividus* (Aiton) Briquet = *lividus*

trifolius var. *lividus* (Aiton) Knocke = *lividus*

trifolius var. *serratifolius* (DC.) Gürke = *argutifolius*

trilobus Lam. = *Coptis trifolia*

triphyllos var. *integrifolius* (DC.) Gürke = *lividus*

triphyllus Lam. var. = *lividus* or *argutifolius*

vaginatus Host = *dumetorum*

vernalis hort. = *niger* 'Vernalis'

vesicarius Aucher

× *viridescens* Schiffner = hybrid (?

atrorubens × viridis)

viridiflorus Stokes = *viridis* ?subsp. *occidentalis*

viridis Linn. subsp. **viridis**

viridis subsp. *dumetorum* (W. & K.) Hayek = *dumetorum*

viridis subsp. **occidentalis** (Reut.) Schiffner

viridis var. *atrorubens* (W. & K.) Kittel = *atrorubens*

viridis var. *bocconei* (Tenore) Baker = *multifidus* subsp. *bocconei*

viridis var. *cupreus* (Host) Neilr. = variant of *atrorubens*

viridis var. *cyclophyllus* A.Br. = *cyclophyllus*

viridis var. *dumetorum* (W. & K.) Sadl. = *dumetorum*

viridis var. *graveolens* (Host) Maly = *odorus*

viridis var. *intermedius* (Guss.) Arcang. = *multifidus* subsp. *bocconei*

viridis var. *intermedius* (Host) Baker = *torquatus*

viridis var. *jacquinianus* A.Br. = *viridis* subsp. *viridis*

viridis var. *laxus* (Host) Kittel = *multifidus* subsp. *istriacus*

viridis var. *multifidus* (Vis.) Vis. = *multifidus* subsp. *multifidus*

viridis var. *odorus* (W. & K.) Kittel = *odorus*

viridis var. *orientalis* (Lam.) Finet & Gagnep. = *orientalis* subsp. *orientalis*

viridis var. *pallidior* Schiffner = hybrid (? *viridis* × *dumetorum*)

viridis var. *pallidus* (Host) Schur = *dumetorum*

viridis var. *purpurascens* (W. & K.) Neilr. = *purpurascens*

viridis var. *smithianus* A.Br. = *viridis* subsp. *occidentalis*

viridis var. *smithianus* forma *maculatus* Salmon = variant of *viridis* subsp. *occidentalis*

viridis var. *subcoloratus* A.Br. = *torquatus*

viridis var. *thibetanus* (Franch.) Finet & Gagnep. = *thibetanus*

APPENDIX C

Suppliers of Hellebores

Blackthorn Nursery (A.R. & S.B. White), Kilmeston, Alresford, Hampshire, SO24 0NL.

Blooms of Bressingham Ltd., Bressingham, Diss, Norfolk, IP22 2AB.

Broadleigh Gardens (Lady Christine Skelmersdale), Barr House, Bishops Hull, Taunton, Somerset, TA4 1AE.

Beth Chatto, White Barn House, Elmstead Market, Colchester, CO7 7DB.

Court Farm Nurseries, Fibrex Nurseries, Honeybourne Road, Pebworth, Nr. Stratford-upon-Avon, Warwick, CV37 8XT.

Margery Fish Plant Nursery, East Lambrook Manor, South Petherton, Somerset, TA13 5HL.

Will McLewin, 42 Bunkers Hill, Romiley, Stockport, SK6 3DS.

J. & E. Parker-Jervis, Marten's Hall Farm, Longworth, Abingdon, Oxon, OX13 5EP.

Washfield Nursery (Elizabeth Strangman), Horns Road, Hawkhurst, Kent, TN18 4QU.

NB: Helen Ballard, who has for many years been raising and supplying fine Hellebores, has asked to be excluded from the above list of suppliers since she has now ceased to trade due to depleted stocks caused by the very heavy demand.

Bibliographical References

AHLBERG, M., The seedling of *Helleborus vesicarius*, in *The Plantsman* 9, 1: 18–20 (1987)

AIRY-SHAW, H.K., *A Dictionary of Flowering Plants and Ferns*, 8th ed. (1973)

ANDERSON, E.B., Hellebores, in *Journ. Roy. Hort. Soc.* 82: 279–293 (1957).

ASCHERSON, P. & GRAEBNER, P., *Synopsis der Mitteleuropäischen Flora* 5, 2: 587–609 (1926).

BAKER, J.G., The Species of Helleborus, in *Gard. Chron.* 1877: 432, 464 (1877).

BALLARD, H., Breeding a Yellow Hellebore, in *The Garden* 112: 45–46 (1987).

BECK, G.R., in *Wiss. Bosn. Herzeg.* 13: 190 (1916).

BENTHAM, G. & HOOKER, J.D., *Genera Plantarum* 1, 1: 6–10 (1862).

BENTLEY, R. & TRIMEN, H., *Medicinal Plants* (1880).

BOISSIER, E., *Flora Orientalis* 1: 63 (1867).

BRAUN, A., New Helleborus species, in *Index Seminum Hort. Bot. Berol.* 1853, appendix: 13–14 (1853).

BRAUN, A. & BOUCHÉ, C., A classification of Helleborus, in *Index Seminum Hort. Bot. Berol.* 1861, appendix: 13–14 (1861).

BRICKELL, C.D. & SHARMAN. F., *The Vanishing Garden*: 120–124. John Murray (1986).

BUSCH, N., in Kuznetzov, Busch & Fomin, *Fl. Cauc. Crit.* 3: 25 (1901).

DAVIS, P.H. & CULLEN, J., in *Flora of Turkey* 1: 96–97 (1965).

DIOSCORIDES, P., *De Materia Medica* (c.77 AD, transl. by Goodyer, J., 1655).

DOSTÁL, J., *Kvetena CSSR* (*Flora of Czechoslovakia*): 135–138 (1950).

FOX STRANGWAYS, W., Synopsis of Helleborus, in *Paxton's Flower Garden* 3: sub t. 82 (1853).

GERARD, J., *Herball* or *Generall Historie of Plantes* (1597).

GROSSHEIM, A.A., *Fl. Kavkaza* 4: 15–16 (1950).

HAMILTON, E., *Flora Homoeopathica* Vol. 1 (1852).

HAYEK, A., Helleborus, in *Prodr. Fl. Penins. Balcan.* 1: 298–300 (1927).

HEGI, G., *Illustr. Fl. Mitteleuropa* 3, 3: 91–107 (1974).

HELLYER, A., Hellebores and Snowdrops (Helen Ballard's nursery described), in *The Garden* 107; 475–477 (1982).

HORT, A., Translation of Theophrastus, *Enquiry into Plants* (1916).

HOST, N. Th., *Fl. Austriaca* 2: 85–91 (1831).

HUTCHINSON, J., *The Families of Flowering Plants*: 493 (1973).

KNUTH, P., *Handbook of Flower Pollination* 2: 1–47 (1908).

KOCH, C., Die Arten der Schwarzen Niesswurz (Helleborus), in *Allg. Gartenzeit.* 1858: 121 *et seq* (1858)

KOCH, C., in *Gard. Chron.* 1874: 118 (1874).

KOCH, C., in *Gard. Chron.* 1874: 480 (1874).

KOLAKOVSKY, A., in *Not. Syst. Geogr. Inst. Bot. Tiflis*, fasc. 5: 7 (1939).

KOMAROV, V.L., Helleborus, in *Fl. USSR* 7: 57–60 (1937), Engl. transl. 7: 46–48 (1970).

LACZA, J.S., Beitrage zur Arealkunde der Ungarischen Helleborus Arten, in *Ann.*

Hist.-Nat. Mus. Nat. Hung. 201–209 (1959).

M.A.F.F., *Poisonous Plants in Britain*, Ref. book 161: 201 (1984).

MALY, K., in *Glasn. Muz. Bosn. i Herceg.* 11: 132 (1899).

MARTINIS, Z., Helleborus in *Fl. Anal. Jugosl.* 1, 2: 231–243 (1973).

MARTINIS, Z., Taxa Nova et Combae Novae Generis Helleborus L. in Flora Yugoslaviae, in *Suppl. Fl. Anal. Jugosl.* 1: 13–16 (1973).

MATHEW, B., A. Gardeners Guide to Hellebores, in *Bull. Alpine Garden Soc.* 35: 1–32 (1967).

MATHEW, B., Hellebores, in *The Garden* 113: 103–110 (1988).

MERXMÜLLER, H. & PODLECH, D., Über die Europäischen Vertreter von Helleborus, in *Feddes Repert. Spec. Nov.* 64: 1–8 (1961).

MEYRICK, W., *New Family Herbal* (1790).

NELSON, E.C., *An Irish Flower Garden*. Boethius Press (1984).

NORTH, P., *Poisonous Plants and Fungi*. Blandford Press (1967).

NOWICKE, J.W. & SKVARLA, J.J., A Palynological study of the genus *Helleborus*, in *Grana* 22: 129–140 (1983).

PIGNATTI, S., *Flora D'Italia* 1: 279–281 (1982).

PLINY THE ELDER, *History of the World*, or *Natural History of Pliny* (23–79 AD, transl. by Holland, 17th c.).

POLUNIN, O. & WALTERS, M., *A Guide to the Vegetation of Britain and Europe*. Oxford University Press (1985).

PRANTL, K., in *Engl. Bot. Jahrb.* 9: 243 (1888).

REICHENBACH, L., *Icones Florae Germanicae* 4: t. 103–112 (1840).

REICHENBACH, L., *Fl. Germ. Excurs.*: 745 (1832).

ROSENHEIM, P., The Genus Helleborus, in *Flora and Silva* 11: 74 (1939).

SĂVULESCU, T., *Flora Republicii Populare Române* 2: 423–430 (1953).

SCHIFFNER, V., Monographia Hellebororum, in *Engl. Bot. Jahrb.* 11: 92–122 (1889), and in *Nova Acta K. Leop.-Carol. Deutsch. Akad. Naturforscher* 56, 1: 1–199 (1890).

SERVETTAZ, O., et al., Osservazioni su *Helleborus viridis s.l.* in Lombardia, in *Suppl. Giorn. Bot. Ital.* 117: 101–103 (1983).

SMITH, C., Breeding Hellebores in Australia, in *The Garden* 111: 118–119 (1986).

SOÓ REZSÖ, *Synopsis Systematico-Geobotanica Florae Vegetationisque Hungariae* 2: 31–33 (1966).

SPACH, E., in *Hist. Nat. Veg.* 3: 312–321 (1839).

THEOPHRASTUS, *Enquiry into Plants* (372–287 BC, Sir Arthur Hort. transl., 1916).

THOMAS, G.S., *Perennial Garden Plants*: 170. J.M. Dent (1982).

TOURNEFORT, J.P. de, *Voyage into the Levant* (1718).

TUTIN, T.G., in *Flora Europaea* 1: 207–208 (1964).

ULBRICH, E., *Blätter für Staudenkunde: Helleborus*. Verein Deutscher Staudenfreunde in der Deutschen Garten-Gesellschaft. Berlin (1938).

WOODVILLE, W., *Medical Botany* (1790).

YEO, P.F., The Nomenclature of *Helleborus lividus* Aiton sens. lat., in *Taxon* 35: 156–161 (1986).

Index

Page numbers for illustrations are shown in bold. Only the main page references to the accepted species (& subsp., vars. etc.) are given. The better-known synonyms are also included here, and the rest can be found in the 'finding list' on p. 171 which shows the species to which they belong.